SHINRAN

Shinran Shonin in Exile

Wooden statue owned by Kogenji (Temple) in
Kokubu, Niigata Prefecture. Sculptor Unknown.

SHINRAN

By
Hyakuzo Kurata

Translated from the Japanese by
Umeyo Hirano

Edited by
Tsumika Maneki

CULTURAL INTERCHANGE INSTITUTE
FOR BUDDHISTS
Honganji Temple, Tsukiji, Chuo-ku,
Tokyo, Japan

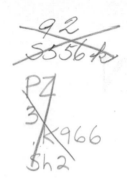

Copyright, March 1964
by CIIB PRESS, Tokyo
First Edition
All rights reserved

EDITOR'S NOTE

During my high school days, as I studied various religious literature, I came across Paul Carus's *The Gospel of the Buddha*, which I read several times with great interest and appreciation.

The following thoughts impressed me very much: Four Noble Truths, Eight-fold Path, Karma ("Nothing can be created nor destroyed"), Nature of Existence (Impermanence, Incompleteness and Soullessness), Dhammapada, Ego and Compassion, and Samsara and Nirvana.

I gradually began to understand the law of Karma, which is life itself, physical and spiritual, a beginningless beginning and an endless end, and began to believe that I am the result of my past actions, and am planting the seed for my future harvest at the same time.

As to my future harvest, that of attaining Nirvana, I considered my past and present actions, and the following of the Eight-fold Path, as taught by Sakyamuni Buddha. The thought of "The eternal cry of man who ever desires to do good and yet fails" began to occupy my mind. Soon I discovered that the actual practice of the Eight-fold Path is very difficult, if not impossible. There was no sense of fulfillment or satisfaction in practice which was limited by my ability and self-control.

As I tried to solve my problem, I was advised to listen to and study the teaching of Shin Buddhism (Shin-shu, Jodo Shin-shu, Shin sect, Hongwanji, the Temple of the Original Vow). Too numerous to name are the leaders who encouraged and helped me at this time of need on my part. I read several books on the life and teaching of St. Shinran very carefully, and came to believe that he has given us the true interpretation of Buddhism for the benefit of all classes of people.

Some of the books I have read from time to time are: *Tannisho* by Tosui Imadate, Saizo Inagaki, and Ryukyo Fujimoto, *Naturalness* by Kenryo Kanamatsu, *The True Meaning of Buddhism* by Ryuchi Fujii, *A Miscellany on the Shin Teaching of Buddhism* by Daisetz Teitaro Suzuki, *The Private Letters of Shinran Shonin* and *The Shoshinge* by Kosho Yamamoto and *Shinran and His Religion of True Faith* by Gendo Nakai.

As I read them, I began to analyze some of St. Shinran's thoughts carefully and slowly: (a) The word " faith " may also be read " true mind." It is not the delusioned and limited mind of man. It is entirely Buddha's mind. When Buddha's mind manifests itself in man, it is called faith. (b) Amida Buddha surrounds all men and all forms of life with infinite compassion and wisdom. (c) Marvelous is the Vow of Amida Buddha! Whether one be young or old, righteous or wicked, literate or illiterate, all shall be saved through

faith and faith alone. (d) If even the virtuous can be
saved, how much more so, the wicked ! This is Amida
Buddha's thought.

At this stage of the development of my mind, I began
to reason gradually and slowly that : (1) Karma, the
law of cause and effect, is truth. (2) My life, physical
and spiritual, will continue this way indefinitely, though
my form may change, if I do nothing for myself, no matter what high ideals I may have. This was of great
concern to me ! At the same time, I was reminded
of St. Shinran's statement : " I am incapable of observing any deeds of merit, and for that reason, my ultimate
abode is none other than hell itself."

I then knew that I had to seek a better understanding
of the ways of St. Shinran, who devoted his life to solv-
ing problems like mine. This was the beginning that
led me to the door of the ministry.

As I tried to follow in Shinran's footsteps and thought
of sharing with others the way to a life of peace, understanding and thanksgiving, it occurred to me that
Shinran (dealing with his life and faith) should be translated into the English language. To accomplish this,
I asked Miss Umeyo Hirano of Kyoto, Japan, to
do the translation, and I am happy to be able to present
this historical novel to the English-speaking public.

This book is a translation of the historical novel *Shinran* by the late Hyakuzo Kurata of Japan, first
published in 1936. Many consider this a unique and
significant interpretation of the Buddhist way of life,
a life of thanksgiving and service through the compassion

and wisdom of Amida Buddha, in the face of poverty and loneliness.

It is based on fragmentary historical records known to date and well known legends, closely and skillfully knitted together by the gifted author into a life story of the founder of Shin Buddhism, and brings out the spirit and faith of St. Shinran.

In presenting this publication to the public, I owe grateful thanks to the Right Reverend Bishop Chitoku Morikawa* of the Honpa Hongwanji Kyodan of Hawaii for his suggestions and encouragement; to Miss Umeyo Hirano of the Osaka City University of Osaka, Japan, for translating from the Japanese into English and for proofreading the manuscript; to the Reverend Tokusui Kotani of the Cultural Interchange Institute for Buddhists of Tokyo, Japan, for making the necessary and detailed arrangements; to Mrs. Iris Mitamura Shiihara of Honolulu, Hawaii, for typing the entire manuscript; and lastly to all those who have led me to this profound teaching of Shin Buddhism.

TSUMIKA MANEKI

September, 1963
Honolulu, Hawaii

* Former President, Ryukoku University, Kyoto, Japan.

FOREWORD

The Rev. Tsumika Maneki, who chose the noble task of seeing this book published, is a member of the English-speaking ministers staff of the Hawaii Honpa Hongwanji Mission and the principal of the Hongwanji Mission School.

The writer of this foreword is deeply impressed in knowing that the Rev. Maneki's father, the late Yokichi Maneki, had at one time served as president of the Board of Directors of the Hilo Hongwanji Mission, and had been a devout follower of the Jodo Shinshu teachings. All the more, the writer takes great pleasure in mentioning that, having been brought up in such a religious family, it is no wonder that the Rev. Maneki has devoted so much of his life to our church.

He was graduated from the University of Hawaii, and served with the Division of Vocational Agriculture, Department of Education ; the Agricultural Extension Service of the University of Hawaii ; and the Farmers Home Administration, U. S. Department of Agriculture.

He graciously accepted the position of President of the Board of Kona Hongwanji Mission and later served as one of the directors of the Hilo Hongwanji Mission. In 1950 he represented the Buddhists of Hawaii at the Conference of World Fellowship of Buddhists held in Ceylon.

A few years later, while he was serving at Hilo Hongwanji Mission, his many years of pursuit in the Dharma were crystalized ; for it was at this time that he decided to follow in the noble steps of the many who have chosen to spread the Nembutsu teachings left for us by Shinran Shonin.

Toward this purpose, he studied at Ryukoku University in Kyoto, and gained the knowledge and qualifications of a minister of the Hongwanji Sect. He then became a minister of the Hawaii Honpa Hongwanji Mission, and immediately assumed the responsibilities of principal of the Hongwanji Mission School of Honolulu.

In considering the Rev. Maneki's intentions in publishing this book and presenting copies to outstanding libraries throughout the world, the writer is convinced that it is the Rev. Maneki's way of making manifest his deep belief in the teachings of Shinran Shonin, and expressing, in his humble way, his appreciation for the unlimited blessings of the Buddha's teachings.

The original book in the Japanese language is indeed so famous that it needs no further mention by the writer.

The translator, Miss Umeyo Hirano, is a graduate of the University of Hawaii who has lived in Japan for many years, teaching the English language. Recently she has devoted herself most faithfully to the study of

Buddhism and Shinshu doctrines as a graduate student of Ryukoku University.

Miss Hirano has had many years of experience in the translation and publication of Buddhist literature, and in the writer's opinion she was a most suitable choice for the work of translation.

I strongly believe that this book will be most effective in spreading the teachings of Shinran Shonin among the peoples of the world, and take this opportunity to express my sincerest Aloha and best wishes.

CHITOKU MORIKAWA

September 17, 1963

Bishop, Honpa Hongwanji
Mission of Hawaii

PUBLISHER'S NOTE

We feel it a great honor to be able to publish *Shinran,* accepting the Reverend Tsumika's request.

In order to promote peace among the different peoples of the world, there must be, above all, a sympathetic understanding of each other's cultures and religions. We sincerely hope that this book will help to bring about a right understanding of Buddhism.

The CIIB Press

CONTENTS

PREFACE

This is a narration of Shinran Shonin's life and faith, written freely as a novel for easy reading. Consequently, it has made use of legends, popular beliefs, and literary imagination, and is not necessarily true to historical facts.

The available facts about Shinran are very vague. If we rely on facts alone, it would be almost impossible to write even a short biography.

Nearly all of his popular biographies are based on legends. The lineage of the Hino family, Tamahi, and Asahime are all legends. Shinran's status on Mount Hiei and the conditions of the Buddhist organizations in Kanto are also very vague. And as for Iyanyo, Sho-amidabutsu, and Lady Hingashi, their lives are as vague as clouds.

Therefore, I thought I would take a step forward and compile all these factors into a story, for I considered it most important to carve in relief the essence of Shinran's faith.

The result was a novel, easy to read, I think, with beautiful and profound contents and rich rhetorical embellishments. I must say that the stories about Iyanyo,

Sho-amidabutsu, and Lady Hingashi are nearly all created by imagination. These people are not mentioned in any documents, except in few words and phrases, and this fact interested the author.

Needless to say, many of the published documentary records concerning the Shonin have been studied. I am especially indebted to Koki Sudo's *Shinran Shonin*.

The work and interest of the author were focused on compiling a story by using all the available literature and free imagination. I am confident that the story has grasped the essence of Shinran Shonin's character and faith.

Hyakuzo KURATA

TRANSLATOR'S NOTE

Hyakuzo Kurata (1891–1943), the author of *Shinran*, was an outstanding dramatist and novelist of modern Japan. Of his many works, *Shinran*, here translated, is a story of the life and faith of Shinran Shonin, the founder of the Shin Buddhism, which advocates the doctrine of salvation through faith in Amida Buddha. Bedridden most of his life, Kurata early turned to humanitarianism and religion, which can be seen in all of his works. I think that *Shinran* is none other than a sincere expression of his own conviction, and it is this that grips the reader.

In translating *Shinran*, I have tried to make as faithful a translation of the original as possible, especially taking pains to be precise in the translation of Buddhist expressions, in which the book abounds and which have little or no equivalent in English.

I express my thanks to Professor Ryukyo Fujimoto of Ryukoku University for kindly helping me with the difficult Buddhist terms, and to Mr. Raymond Maneki of Honolulu, Hawaii, for his help in improving the English. By translating this book, I think I have done a good thing for myself, more than for anybody

else, since it helped me immensely to understand Shinran Shonin, the great man.   Because of this, I thank the
Reverend Tsumika Maneki for asking me to do the
translation.

Umeyo HIRANO

Kyoto, Japan
August 28, 1963

Chapter 1

THOUGH FLOWERS BLOOM

" Though flowers bloom beautifully, they soon fall.
Man's life is just as changeable," so goes the saying.
Only the greatest of sages know that there is nothing
lasting in this world of ours; consequently, they can live
free of all mental attachments. The waves of rebirth
began billions of years ago and will never come to an end.
Only those followers of the Nembutsu[1] who have been
given the insight into Truth can drift with the tide, and
reach their destination safely. They make the voyage
gently and easily without any effort, becoming one with
the Law of birth-and-death. To them, an adverse
wind is at once a fair wind.

Such a very rare sage was born in the third year of
Shoan[2], in the reign of Emperor Takakura, at a place
called Hino in the village of Daigo, in the outskirts of
Kyoto, Uji County, in the province of Yamashiro.
At that time the world was, as usual, one of constant
change, in which the waves of mutability were raging.

[1] Jodo School of Buddhism.
[2] 1173 A.D.

It was more than ten years after the wars of Hogen and Heiji, and the Heikes were at the height of their prosperity. Their life of luxury had already become corrupted, and complaints were beginning to mount.

The most unfortunate were the Fujiwaras. Though they still held positions of distinction from custom and practice, they no longer had any real power. Matters of grave concern to the state were all decided by the dictatorship of the Heike clan, which had military strength. If anything displeased Kiyomori[1], he would go to the capital with soldiers, hold a demonstration, and make demands by force.

The Fujiwaras could do nothing. The worldly storm raged most fiercely against them. They had to endure the misfortune of the family's downfall and the perpetual insults received in public, their honor trampled.

Shinran Shonin was born a son of Arinori Hino, who belonged to the unfortunate Fujiwara clan. They had social standing but no power nor wealth. Their position was miserable in the people's eyes. Their circumstances cast a shadow on the family, a melancholy air drifting about the house.

We can understand this feeling of gloom when we read Kanezane Kujo's diary called " Gyokuyo," which says :

" 14th day. Today Nyudo Shokoku [i.e. Kiyomori] came to the capital. There are several hundred warriors on horseback. Nobody knows what they are for. The

[1] Leader of Heike clan.

confusion in the city is incomparable. All over the city people are transporting building materials to east and west. These are troubled times, indeed.

" 15th day. At 4 a.m. an officer of the Imperial Household reported the dismissal of Kanpaku (chief advisor to the Emperor) Motofusa, and the appointment of Motomichi, the Lord Keeper of the Privy Seal, to the concurrent post of Kanpaku. The official posts of thirty-nine personal attendants of the retired Monk-Emperor have been taken away. This is because after the death of Shigemori, the province of Echizen was made public land. Today when night came, the Empress and the Crown Prince visited the Hachijo Palace, and it's reported that they will together go to Kyushu.

" 22nd day. The former Kanpaku, who has entered the priesthood, and his wife, who has become a nun, heard all about this and wept bitterly. The area enclosed by Tominokoji Street on the east, Rokujo Street on the south, Sujaku Avenue on the west and the Palace on the north was burned down. This is an unheard-of event, and the remains after the fire look quite serious: fires, burglaries, mass disturbances, agitation between high and low. These are extremely turbulent days, and beyond human power.

" May 1st. Several burglars broke into the Imperial Palace and carried away many things, besides setting fire to the buildings. There is great confusion in the Imperial Household. Has fortune come to an end? There is no end to our grief. Is our country now to go to ruin? I am only ashamed of my fate of having been born in these troublous times."

Such was the condition of the times. A court noble.

Chapter 2

A REBELLIOUS SPIRIT

Among the falling nobles, however, there were some who had firm character. There were some who had a strong sense of justice and could not bear the outrageous behavior of the Heikes. Shinran's father, Arinori Hino, was one of them.

Arinori lived at Hino in the County of Uji. The name Uji reminds one of the loyal army raised by the Third-rank Yorimasa of the Minamoto clan. His was the first revolt against the arrogant Heikes. It was this revolt that sounded an alarm against their ears, warning them that public opinion censured the luxury of the Heikes, and that complaints would be heard everywhere throughout the country. The fall of the Heike clan started at this time.

Arinori Hino joined this loyal army raised by the Third-rank Yorimasa. Prince Mochihito of Takakura-no-miya confined himself in the Onjoji (Temple), located at the foot of Mount Nagara, together with Yorimasa and his son and several hundred horsemen.

The monks on Mount Hiei gathered together,

ringing the great bell. They wore long swords, carried bows and arrows and guarded the large and small barriers. As a result, it was reported that the monk-soldiers of Kofukuji (Temple) of Nara would also rise.

On the other hand, Heike officers had gathered at the mansion of Rokuhara and were busy holding a war council, saying that the rebels were like straws in the wind. They summoned soldiers from Kaido and Hokuriku and the blackguards of Totsugawa, and stationed troops on the eastern and western slopes of Mount Hiei.

At that time at Arinori's residence, Lady Kikko, Shinran's mother, was confined to bed with a serious illness. Shinran, who was called Matsuwaka-maru in his childhood, was at his mother's bedside with his younger brother, Asa-maru, trying to ease her pain.

Lady Kikko knew that she could not recover. She also knew that her husband was compelled to raise a loyal army, but that they had hardly any chance of success against the flourishing Heikes. Reports had all said, as had been expected, that the odds were against them. Then came the news that they had been completely defeated at Byodoin (Temple), Uji. Her husband would not return alive, she feared.

The bell of Hokaiji (Temple) echoed the sound of mutability to her bedside. She who was about to die had expected this. But what would become of the little children? This worried her more than anything else.

Matsuwaka-maru sat at his mother's bedside sadly, and, though a mere child, felt sad as the breeze moved the curtain, wafting the smell of medicine. There had been something noble about his young face ever since his birth.

The mother remembered the miraculous dream at the time of his birth. It was at midnight on the 2nd of May in the second year of Shoan. In her dream she saw a great light come and shine around her. And she heard a voice calling her.

" Lady Kikko. Lady kikko."

Startled, she looked up and saw the beautiful figure of Nyoirin Kannon Bodhisattva wearing a dazzling diadem. Lady Kikko threw herself at the feet of the Bodhisattva.

The Kannon said: " You will bear a son through predestination for there is a well of piety within you. He will become a light that will save all common mortals, both good and bad, men and women, in these latter days of Buddhism. But be careful not to tell this to anybody."

She dreamed that she was given a five-needled pine branch. Then she awoke. A strange smell of incense had filled the room.

Then on May 21 the following year Matsuwaka-maru was born. She was struck with awe and did not say anything about the dream to anyone, not even to Matsuwaka-maru.

" But I shall soon die. Should I tell about it to Matsuwaka-maru?" she thought to herself.

" No. What the Buddha said is awesome. I shall keep it to myself to my last moment."

" But what will become of this child who is going to be an orphan? Would he not go astray from the right way? Could he be led into the Law of the Buddha?" She was at a loss again.

She sadly looked at the five-colored thread, a charm for the prolongation of life, swaying at her bedside.

Just then Noritsuna Fujiwara, her husband's elder brother, came to see her.

" How is your illness?"

" It is a matter of today or tomorrow. What worries me is the future of my children. I cannot die because of that uncertainty."

" As for that matter, please keep your heart at ease. I will look after them always in place of Arinori. Only I'm sorry for my brother Arinori. . . ."

Lady Kikko held her breath.

" What has happened to him?"

" He took his own life at Onjoji last night."

She said nothing for some time.

" He had long prepared for it. Arinori must be satisfied," said Lady Kikko after a while.

Holding back his tears, Noritsuna drew near her, his *eboshi*[1] bending, and spoke with deep sympathy.

" Now you can go peacefully. As for your children, this uncle will look after them without fail."

" Then I have nothing to worry about. I want to follow Arinori."

Her voice showed that she had resigned completely to her fate.

[1] A kind of headgear

The sobbing of the ladies-in-attendance was heard outside the curtained screens.

In this way Matsuwaka-maru lost both his father and mother.

Shinran might have inherited the rebellious spirit, which is an outstanding element of his personality, from his father.

Chapter 3

A YOUNG SHOOT OF THE
BUDDHA'S LAW

Little Matsuwaka-maru crouched a long time in front of the two newly-built mounds of graves in the compounds of Hokaiji (Temple) in worship—his head drooped. His hair was done in childish fashion.

" Why must man die? Where is my father, who used to pat my head and praise my writing practice? Where is my mother who, till a few months ago, was with me day and night as the shadow follows the form ; and brought me up, holding me in her arms, giving me a bath, scolding me and caressing me? Is it impossible to see them again no matter how long I wait? Is it right to have to face such a terrible fate? This is something I cannot endure. I can endure any hardship and hunger. But this one thing is impossible to endure. It is too sad to bear.

" If they tell me they would let me see my parents if I did such and such a thing, I would do it no matter how difficult. If I could see them if I waited, I would wait. But isn't it unreasonable to say that I shall never see my dear father and mother again? Have people all borne such sadness from ancient times? People all say it cannot be helped. But there are sufferings which man can bear in his heart, and those which he cannot bear. This is a suffering of the heart which one cannot endure."

Matsuwaka-maru's innocent mind could not understand this, no matter how hard he tried.

Whenever he had time, he went to the Hino family's graveyard and bowed his head and clasped his tiny hands to pray. The evening glow shone and colored the gravestones that were piled one upon the other. The lonely sound of the breeze in the pine trees could be heard. Even the cawing of the crows sounded sad.

He saw in the distance the white stream, Hitsugawa, flowing through the village of Hino. Where was the stream going? He remembered that his mother used to say that human beings were like bubbles.

" What province is that beyond the Kasatori ranges? Might I not meet Father and Mother if I crossed that mountain and walked on and on? "

To Matsuwaka-maru the way looked far and hopeless.

He took some mud and began to knead it into an image of a Buddha. He recalled the Buddha's image which he had made at the Nehan festival[1] when he was five years old, and which his mother had especially praised.

His mind was somewhat comforted. He was absorbed in making the Buddha's image and forgot the

[1] The anniversary of the death of Sakyamuni Buddha.

passage of time.

Uncle Noritsuna was glad of Matsuwaka-maru's strong filial affection, but it worried him because the child yearned after his parents and grieved so much for them. This day, too, as the child was late in coming home, he came to the graveyard and saw Matsuwaka-maru absorbed in shaping the image.

The child made an image of the Buddha and made it stand by the side of his parents' graves. He then offered wild daisies to the graves, and clasped his hands.

The good uncle was moved to tears. He cleared his throat.

Matsuwaka-maru turned. He blushed childishly.

" Matsuwaka-maru, you really miss your father and mother, don't you? "

" Yes, I do miss them."

" For what do you make the Buddha's image? "

" I'm told that the Buddha grants our requests. So I worship it."

" What do you say in your worship? "

" I say, please let me see Father and Mother once more."

" Mm." The uncle pondered. " But that will not be granted, I'm afraid."

" Uncle, why won't it? "

" Well, then," the uncle said, and as if admonishing the child, he continued, " To hope to see your parents is a delusion. To brush aside such delusion and to make your heart as clear as that moon over there—that is the Buddha's teaching."

Matsuwaka-maru's expression was a mixture of extreme loneliness and reverence.

" I shall give you elementary lessons in Buddhist scriptures little by little from now on, for you are intelligent."

" Please teach me."

From that day Noritsuna began to teach the child the reading of the *Suddharma-Pundarika Sutra*[1]. Matsuwaka-maru memorized the lessons with natural ease, as naturally as seeds fall in the fields.

After Matsuwaka-maru had learned the chapter " Shiyo-hon " he recited it morning and evening for the repose of his dead father and mother.

He was taught the *Suddharma-Pundarika Sutra* every day, and by the end of the year he knew twenty-eight chapters.

Noritsuna loved the boy's intelligence and made him learn Chinese classics from a scholar named Tadamichi Hino. The child first learned *Hsiao-ching*[2] and finished *Ta-hsueh*[3] and *Lun-yu*[4] thoroughly, to the astonishment of his teacher. To this child prodigy, finishing a book meant the same thing as reciting it from memory.

But meanwhile, Matsuwaka-maru could not forget the memory of his father and mother. He especially longed for his mother.

He went inside the curtained screens where his sick

[1] Lotus Sutra.

[2] The Book of Filial Duty.

[3] One of the Four Chinese Classics.

[4] The Discourse of Confucius.

mother had lain, and thought of by-gone days.   He took out his mother's clothes and smelt the scent that still remained in them.   He went into the closet and pulled out her mirror and comb and yearned for her.   He had realized in his young mind how sad separation was, how tormenting it was not to be able to meet one whom he loved.

Chapter 4

CUTTING OFF THE BLACK HAIR

The world was ceaselessly changing. The army which Minamoto Yorimasa had raised was defeated. Kiyomori suddenly made a reckless plan to move the capital to Fukuhara. Not only the Emperor but all the hundreds of court-nobles and common people were opposed to this, but he did not listen to them, and finally on June 2 removed the capital to Fukuhara. The citizens' grief and confusion then were something one had never heard of before.

Kiyomori, like a madman, burned down Onjoji (Temple). Moreover, he conquered Kofukuji (Temple) in Nara, killed several thousand monks, and damaged the great image of the Buddha. While the public burned with indignation, a messenger arrived on horseback on September 2 with the report that Yoritomo had raised an army, obeying Prince Mochihito's command.

A half-year had not yet passed, when the Emperor came back to Kyoto[1], leaving the new capital Fukuhara,

---

[1] This means that the capital was moved back to Kyoto by Kiyomori.

where construction had not yet been completed. Indeed, this was an extremely rash undertaking exactly like " issuing an order in the morning and repealing it in the evening." The world had begun to change rapidly like a revolving lantern[1].

On January 24 of the new year, Kiso Yoshinaka rose in revolt, and Munemori, who had hoped to conquer, came back utterly defeated. In the meantime Kiyomori was attacked by an illness of unknown origin and died on February 4. The country was filled with the foreboding that a disturbance might break out at any moment.

As for Matsuwaka-maru, however, as he learned more of the *Pundarika Sutra*, his desire for something constant and everylasting, outside the world of such changes, became stronger.

His uncle Noritsuna could not escape from the worldly waves of turmoil. Attending an ex-Emperor, he moved to Fukuhara and then back to Kyoto. The following year, the ex-Emperor passed away. The waves of adversity came to the court-noble's life. These things helped to persuade Matsuwaka-maru to renounce the world.

" Uncle, I want to enter the priesthood."

" What are you saying? " Noritsuna was startled.

"As I learn the *Pundarika Sutra* from you, the teaching of the Buddha appeals to me greatly. Having no father

[1] A paper lantern with cut-out pictures pasted on an inner frame, which constantly revolves by means of the paper windmill attached to it.

and mother, I wish to enter the priesthood and serve the Buddha personally."

" Your desire is all very well, but it is no easy matter to renounce the world.   With your talent, you can easily learn the Sutras as a layman and at the same time enter the government service and rise in the world.   So give up the idea of becoming a priest."

" No, I have no desire to rise in the world.   I only wish to become a priest and serve the Buddha and pray for the repose of my dead father and mother."

Noritsuna thought over the matter, for Matsuwaka-maru seemed to be absorbed in thought.

" If it is such a carefully-considered request, I might give you permission.   But are you determined to carry it out? "

" I will be the Buddha's disciple all my life."

" Until you become a priest of renown? "

" That may not be possible, but I will promise to seek the path of the Buddha's Law all my life."

Noritsuna, studying Matsuwaka-maru's expression, realized that the child was destined to be a disciple of the Buddha, so he gave his permission.

Noritsuna took Matsuwaka-maru to Shoren-in (Temple) at Awadaguchi.   There he begged Abbot Jichin, whom he respected, to make the child his disciple.   In the garden the cherry-trees were in full bloom.

The Abbot kept his eyes on Matsuwaka-maru as he listened to Noritsuna's detailed explanation of the youth's circumstances.   But like the high priest of the Tendai Sect that he was, he did not consent to an easy acceptance without an examination. Even this child had to undergo a test and present his answers.

The Abbot said in a severe tone, " Those who wish to be initiated into the Tendai Sect must first undergo a preliminary education for nine years as laymen, and then after obtaining the Government's permission, can take the tonsure.

He said this, however, to test the child. What would the nine-year-old boy say?

The child quickly wrote a *tanka*[1] on a piece of pocket paper, and gave it to the Abbot through Noritsuna. It was as follows:

> " To think that there is a tomorrow
>   Is like the short-lived cherry blossoms:
>   A storm might come in the night
>   And scatter them!"

The Abbot smiled and nodded. A great priest is always delighted to receive a promising disciple.

He immediately had the formalities arranged at the Government office, and decided to perform the ordination rites for the child that very day.

Fragrant water was first sprinkled on the ground. Draperies were hung on the pillars on four sides. Matsuwaka-maru took off his *suikan* robe[2] of red-plum color and wore a plain silk robe and took the seat provided for him. Abbot Jichin, in red robe and three-corded stole, sat in the seat in front.

---

[1] A short poem of 31 syllables.

[2] An informal robe of the nobles, worn with loose, gathered trousers.

Matsuwaka-maru clasped his hands, facing the direction of his home and recited :

" I abandon worldly indebtedness and enter the Unconditioned Law.   This is the true repayment."

He then went up to the Acarya[1], reciting, " I take my refuge in the Honored One, and I shall liberate myself from the sufferings of the Triple World."

Thereupon two monks with torches stepped forward to Matsuwaka-maru's right side and left side respectively. The Acarya then divided the child's hair and poured warm water over it and withdrew.   Abbot Jichin stood up quietly and went and stood behind Matsuwaka-maru. He took the razor and shaved the front part of the head. He then gave the razor to the Acarya and returned to his seat.

The Acarya then shaved off the rest of the divided hair. The thick black hair, which had hung to Matsuwaka-maru's shoulders, like a symbol of worldly affairs, was all shaved off, and there was now the bare scalp of a priestling.

The Abbot gave a black robe and a stole, and the name ' Hannen ' to this new convert.

In this way the ordination ceremony came to an end.

Who would pine for the black hair now?   Had he not become one of the Three Sacred Treasures, which even an emperor would respect?   Thus thought Noritsuna, but in his heart there was a vague feeling of sadness.   What would the child's parents have thought,

---

[1] A master in esoteric Buddhism, skilled in mystic practices.

if they could have seen Matsuwaka-maru in his new life?

Noritsuna thought about it as he quietly took his leave of Matsuwaka-maru. Adjusting the neckband of his dark gray *naoshi*[1] robe, he got into his waiting carriage.

[1] An everyday robe of the high nobles, worn with loose, gathered trousers, and a high headdress.

Chapter 5

AS A YOUNG STUDENT

Hannen had already given himself up to the Buddha. From this day he was to live the pure, serene life of the temple as a disciple of the Buddha.

Hannen, who had become a little monk with a shiny head like the spring view of a hill, devoted himself to daily tasks at Shoren-in (Temple), cherishing a sad fantasy.

The cherry blossoms fell, and then came the season of fresh green leaves and early summer rain. Then it was summer everywhere around Awadaguchi, and frogs began to croak.

Hannen stood in a corridor connecting two buildings of the temple, and gazed at the surface of the pond, where ripples were made by the rain. Lotus buds and flowers lightly floated on the water. In the corridor were beautiful framed pictures of a high-ranking monk in a purple robe, and a court lady in a red robe, together with her *tanka*.

He could not help feeling that the woman's picture was that of his mother. The gentle smile, the intelligent eyes, and the long black hair all reminded him of his kind mother. She had carried him in her arms. He felt like resting his head on this noble-woman's chest and crying for hours.

"Hannen."

Suddenly he heard his teacher's voice. Abbot Jichin had approached unnoticed and was standing behind him.

"Is it you, Teacher?"

"What are you doing?"

"The lotus flowers are so beautiful . . ."

"Hm," said the Abbot, looking at the little monk. "Do you know the expression, 'The delight of the first opening of the lotus flower'?"

"No, I do not."

"Those who have faith but are negligent can go to the Pure Land, but have to live in a borderland for eight hundred years before they are permitted to see the Buddha, like the lotus flowers that first bloom, surrounded by buds."

Hannen's head drooped.

"'Abandoning all our indebtedness, we enter the Unconditioned Law. This is the real repayment.' Under no circumstances go astray of the right way." So saying, he walked quietly away.

The young monk yielded to the clear insight of his teacher. A feeling of shame filled his heart.

The bell rang, and he saw monks walking in silence toward the main temple for the service.

From that time on, Hannen gave up longing for home,

and devoted himself to his studies. Seeing that the boy's abilities were extraordinary, Abbot Jichin finally brought him to Mount Hiei, and breaking precedence, had him undergo the consecration of the Endon.[1]

At last Hannen had formally become a monk. He was to live in Daijo-in (Temple) of Toto on Mount Hiei.

He learned *Shikyogi*[2], *Shoshikan*[2] and *Sandaibu*[2] from Jogon Hoin, who was well-known as a scholar. He also studied the three sects, Tendai, Shingon and Busshin. Gradually his studies became more profound and exhaustive. Days and months passed as he studied with enthusiasm.

The world outside the temple walls went on changing. The Heike clan, which had lived in the lap of luxury, were now heading straight for a downfall. In July, in the second year of Juei, they could not repulse Kiso Yoshinaka's army, and the whole clan had to flee by boat to Chikushi. In the eastern district, Yoritomo was so powerful that he seemed like a dragon rising up into the clouds.

Kiso Yoshinaka's power evaporated like the morning dew. In January of the following year, the first year of Gwanreki, the forces of Yoshitsune and Yoritomo forced Yoshinaka to flee from the capital to Fukada in Awazu. His powerful army, which was once said to be like the rising sun, came to a tragic end, exactly like Hsiang-yu of Chu in China.

[1] Perfect precepts.
[2] Buddhist texts.

Hannen, the young student, applied himself day and
night to studies, indifferent to worldly disturbances. It
was at this time that he studied Buddhist realism and
idealism under Myozen and Kakuun. He did not neglect the esoteric practice, either. The great scholar
Myozen Hoin of the mountain was its great authority.

The world did not stop its terrible shifts and changes.
The Heike's sea forces were utterly defeated. Nii-no-
ama drowned herself in the sea of Dan-no-ura, carrying
the infant Emperor Antoku in her arms. Every member
of the Heike clan sank to the bottom of the sea.

Yoshitsune came back to the capital, a triumphant
general, receiving the greatest honor and fame of the
age, and enjoying the favor of the retired Monk-Emperor.
But this lasted only a short time, for he fell into his
brother Yoritomo's displeasure and had to flee toward
northern Oshu.

Hannen thought of the happiness of the people who
sought the eternal truth, standing apart from the bus-
tling, changing world. This was a privilege of the super-
worldly monks. He thought how profound and bot-
tomless Buddhist learning was. To young, energetic
Hannen, the very fact that the Buddha's Law was so
inconceivable and difficult to master, made it all the
more a challenging subject of his study.

In April, in the 7th year of Kenkyu, he entered for
the first time the large archives of Kofukuji (Temple)
in Nara, and went over the complete collection of
Buddhist scriptures. He sat among the scriptures and
eagerly fed his insatiable intellellectual appetite. It was

the greatest delight to him to be absorbed in reading under the lamplight the expositions and commentaries by men of virtue of ancient days.

Having spent half a year in the archives, he left finally in November and returned to Mount Hiei. Thenceforth he concentrated his attention upon the Busshin Sect.

In this way, his store of knowledge became larger, like a rolling snowball.

Chapter 6

HANNEN'S MENTAL STRUGGLE

Young Hannen in light traveling clothes left the village of Ikaruga, and instead of heading for the Kyoto Highway, took the Tatsuta Road for Oji. He had formed a pleasant plan in his mind when he started on this pilgrimage to the southern city, Nara. It was to confine himself in the mausoleum of Prince Shotoku for prayer.

After passing a valley in the Futago mountains and reaching the village of Shinaga, he immediately went to Eifukuji (Temple) and told the assistant priest the object of his visit.

At the mausoleum, autumn colors were everywhere, and the red leaves were beautiful. He looked up and saw wild geese sailing across the sky. The mausoleum enshrining Prince Shotoku was on the top of a hill.

Hannen cleansed himself in the water of a mountain stream, where red leaves were floating down. After purifying himself with incense, he walked into the sacred mausoleum in awe and reverence.

In the cave were enshrined three stone coffins, namely, Prince Shotoku's in the eastern side, his mother, Empress

Anahobe-no-hashito's in the center, and his wife, Princess Hashiwade-no-omihime's in the western side.

Hannen was struck by a strange feeling. He felt himself becoming tense as he walked up a passage. Bronze lanterns with engravings of lions shone dimly in the interior of the sanctuary, giving it a dreamlike beauty.

His long-cherished adoration of Prince Shotoku came springing afresh over him. Hannen fell on his knees in spite of himself and placed his forehead on the floor. Feelings of reverence and awe overcame him.

Among great scholars, he had grown to feel confident and secure. As his fame spread on Mount Hiei, he had been to Nara, Kawachi, Yamato, and Naniwa to meet Buddhist scholars of other schools, and had been received with respect and honor.

But the moment he had entered this sacred mausoleum, he was aware of a mysterious pressure that made him feel small and insignificant. The strength of ancient sages and holy men, the virtues of the Imperial House, the glory of the Throne as the ancestor of his nation— all these seemed like a light all around him.

In this sanctuary, Hannen sat and fasted for seven nights and seven days with a reverent, whole-hearted devotion.

Finally at about midnight on the seventh day, as his mind became perfectly clear, he felt as if his soul left him and moved about the sanctuary. He was enraptured in an unreal, fantastic land, when suddenly he heard a quiet voice which said:

" Hannen, Hannen."

He was wondering whether he had imagined the voice, when rays of light suddenly illuminated the sanctuary.

Hannen was struck with awe and fell to the floor, for he saw the majestic and divine figure of Prince Shotoku standing there, enveloped in brilliant light.

The voice seemed to say: " Listen to what I say. Your life will last for ten-odd years.   As soon as it ends, you will be born in the Pure Land.   Zenshin,[1] you will be a true Bodhisattva."

Hannen listened to the voice, penetrating to the bottom of his heart, when suddenly the light went out.   In the sanctuary only the taper burned in the quiet autumn night.

It was hard for Hannen to solve the meaning of his dream.   The words, " Your life will last ten-odd years " shook him deeply.

Until now he had never thought deeply about his death.   He had devoted himself to Buddhist learning, and had spent months studying Sutras and their commentaries, going into the minutest details.

As a result of these studies, he achieved the reputation of a genius.   He had expected in his heart that if he went on thus and lived out a natural life, it would not be difficult to become the foremost scholar on Mount Hiei.

But what a blow it had been to hear that he had only about ten years to live ! He felt altogether unprepared.

He recalled the words: "As soon as your life ends,

[1] Hannen's later name.

you will be born in the Pure Land." But to his shame, he had not yet acquired faith and enlightenment. This was because his way of learning was not a matter of personal experience, but wholly that of the intellect. It was because his motive was knowledge rather than attaining enlightenment or being born in the Pure Land.

In a word, he had not yet freed himself from the enslavement of birth-and-death. So naturally he felt upset to know that death would approach in ten years or so.

He felt as though he had been beaten on the head with a hammer. He felt his self-assurance falling to pieces. He lost confidence in himself.

In contrast to the light steps with which he first started on his trip, he returned to the mountain feeling gloomy and uneasy.

However, he kept the dream to himself, and worried alone.

Chapter 7

THE WINTER MOON AND THE
DRAGON WOMAN

A turning point was coming in Hannen's life. He felt it drawing near. He found things were somehow out of order in his mind and the world around him. "The Buddha's means of salvation"—the power in which he believed in his later life—had been guiding his life.

He could not sit still. When he sat before the Sutras with the object "to free himself from the enslavement of birth-and-death" and "to be reborn into the Pure Land," there was always impatience, frustration and dissatisfaction (like wanting to scratch one's itching foot from over the shoes, so to speak).

He felt it would be pointless to remain as he was.

"Is not my life to last for only ten years or so? What good will it do to minutely understand the commentaries on the Sutras? If learning is of no use in transcending birth-and-death, and in being reborn into the Pure Land, is it any better than a pastime, like piling up bricks?"

On this day he went down the mountain as far as Sakamoto, wrapped in pessimistic thoughts.

" Those poets in the *Manyoshu Anthology* who regretted that the capital of Shiga had gone to ruin—they are now merely a subject to talk. Only the waves of the lake are washing the shores of Ishiyama and Karasaki as in the old days. . . . The eternity of nature, the frailty of man ! Were those people, too, as depressed in mind as I am now?

"At Seta the lake water flows down to Uji. O, that Uji ! There my father died in a battle he could not avoid. Kiyomori, his bitter enemy, is also dead and gone now.

" Isn't everything a dream, a bubble-like image? What meaning is there in life? What is learning good for, in the first place? "

Doubts about life filled his mind.

He made his way home with heavy steps. Night had completely fallen at the foot of the mountain. When he was about to start climbing, after passing a field of withered pampas grass, Hannen encountered a woman.

The winter moon shone on her face. She looked pale and strangely beautiful.

" Reverend Monk," she addressed Hannen.

" I have a favor to ask of you. I am suffering from delusion for some reason. Will you please deliver me from it? "

" I am yet far from perfect in discipline," he answered. " I don't have the ability to do it."

" Then please take me to Mount Hiei. There must be great monks and Sutras there. I shall search for sages who can save me."

Hannen was perplexed.

" Don't you know? " he said. " Women are not admitted to the mountain."

" How regrettable ! " said the woman in a choked voice. " But women suffer as much as men. Then, by what means can women be saved? "

Hannen was unable to answer.

" Even in the Buddha's compassion, are we women left out? "

Hannen had no words to reply.

"' How absurd ! " Her voice changed from reproach to scorn. " I see there is not one sage on the mountain who can deliver women. Then I shall look elsewhere for him."

" No. Wherever you may search, there will not be any sage in Japan able to save women, who are more easily emotionally disturbed than men."

" How distressing ! " She began to sob, shedding large tears. " Then I will have to wait under the lake until the appearance of a great sage who can save us."

And the dragon-like woman ran toward the lake.

Hannen felt a chill creep over him. He hurried back to his temple on the mountain.

Was it a human being or a dragon that he had seen? 1t was most strange. He kept this secret to himself and never talked about it to others.

He investigated biographies of ancient sages. He

found that there were many examples of sages having seen strange phenomena. Kobo Daishi[1] was one of them. Dengyo Daishi[2] was another. Hannen thought about the dream prophecy at Shinaga and the appearance of the woman. They were all extraordinary, and he could not help feeling apprehensive. His search after truth became more serious and intensive.

In spite of his mental agitation, his reputation on the mountain went on growing. When he lectured on *Shoshikan*[3] at Kamurodani, Yokawa, in answer to his friends' request, the scholars throughout the mountain were speechless with admiration. They all said he was surely the greatest genius of Mount Hiei.

Even his teacher Jichin began to speak highly of him. And finally after being reported to the Throne, he was appointed to the rank of Sho-sozu, and to the post of abbot of the Emperor-patronized monastery, Shokoin, at Higashiyama on Mount Hiei.

One day as Hannen happened to open a book which he drew from a shelf, he found a letter written to Eshin Sozu by his mother. It read as follows:

"After you went up to the mountain, I missed you very much day and night, but I felt happy to have made you a noble monk. However, you soon came in contact with the Imperial Court and were promoted to higher ranks. It is regrettable that you have become a sage of such great renown and wealth, so as to wear

[1] Founder of Shingon Sect.

[2] Founder of Nippon Tendai.

[3] Tendai Daishi's smaller volume on Shikan (meditation).

purple and blue robes, and to read Sutras before the
Emperor, and to receive offerings. I have sent you
off so that you might make great efforts to attain deliverance, living in a humble cottage under a tree, wearing grass robes, eating simple foods, cutting wood, and
gathering fallen leaves. Instead you are prospering,
coming in contact with the Court, preaching for the
sake of obtaining official rank and reputation. You
are not working toward enlightenment, but going back
to a life of bondage, enslaved by transmigration.

" Please seek deliverance in the next life, by making
a real, honest-to-goodness effort on your part, for now
you have encountered the teachings of the Buddha,
which I understand are as difficult to encounter as
discovering the rare Udumbara[1] flower. What good
does it do to become known among people who are
overcome by delusions in this dreamlike world? Please
distinguish yourself before the Buddha by attaining
enlightenment forever."

Hannen shut the book and closed his eyes, recalling
his dead mother. He could not help feeling that she,
too, like Eshin Sozu's mother, would reprimand him if
she were alive.

Was he not also absorbed in learning for fame and
wealth, and stained by the atmosphere around him?
Had he not wasted years in studying the minor trifles
of the Sutras, forgetting the discipline for the true enlightenment, the search for the way to attain rebirth
into the Pure Land, that vital problem of delivering
himself?

[1] It is said that this flower blossoms only once in 3,000 years.

He now knew he had to change his attitude toward the search after truth. It was the deliverance from birth-and-death that should be the primary aim of his Buddhist practices, and the only one that mattered. All other problems were secondary.

He resolved to make a fresh start, discarding feelings like the pride of knowledge. What could reputation and wealth do? What could self-satisfaction do? To a Buddhist student, the only purpose should be that of becoming a Buddha. This alone had been the object of his entering the priesthood, and should have been the goal to be sought all his life. And this would be the true repayment of his indebtedness.

Hannen realized for the first time that he could put his heart and soul into his search for truth. He realized that he was now on the right path.

Chapter 8

IN THE DARKNESS

It seemed strange. Since he began searching for the real path of life, he began to see that on the mountain, where he had thought culture and religion were blooming, there was nothing but vain architecture and ostentation. Indeed, there were on the mountain solemnity of the Buddhist Law, the stern laws and regulations, the temple buildings of unsurpassed magnificence, the archives filled with volumes of Sutras, and the dignity of the monks in government service. But of what use would all these be in attaining one's rebirth into the Pure Land? They would greatly contribute toward spreading culture. But how would they develop one's enlightenment?

He had to conclude that most people were doing nothing but wasting time. The monks were pursuing their studies, learning rituals, seeking supernatural power. But they were not searching for a path that would free themselves from the enslavement of birth-and-death.

Furthermore, there were on Mount Hiei several thousand people with weapons, devoting themselves to fights, making one wonder if they were soldiers or blackguards. Whenever a political change occurred in the capital, the masses of these monks on the mountain were involved. It was so when Yorimasa revolted, and also when Kiso Yoshinaka's forces broke into the city.

The large bell of the Great Lecture Hall would be rung, and the monks would immediately turn into soldiers. And they would act, not to defend the Buddhist Law or justice, but in the interests of their Order. For this purpose, even Prince Mochihito, who had confined himself in Onjoji (Temple), was betrayed and forsaken overnight. It was because of this also that Yorimasa's heroic deed ended in failure.

In the first place, there were too many ranks and divisions for the monks. Therefore, promotion to a higher rank became each man's aim. Those of higher rank invariably frequented the houses of those who held political power, and bribery was often involved. As each rank differed in power, there was bound to be a continuous struggle for supremacy. This was worse than bribery.

And what had these things to do with the vital problem of attaining rebirth into the Pure Land?

But there were values in the Sutras and the moral precepts, he thought. He had to hold on to them tightly.

All the monks read the scriptures for learning and observed the moral precepts to attain supernatural power. He himself, shameful to say, had been doing the same thing.

But from now on he was going to read the scriptures

and observe the precepts for the sake of rebirth into the Pure Land, of attaining deliverance. This alone could give significance to his life on the mountain.

With this object now clear in mind, Hannen began to re-read the scriptures. But what exaggeration, what roundabout ways, and waste there were here! What arguments and speculation which were troublesome, varied and incomprehensible! In self-glorification and rhetoric, perhaps there could be no treasure house so rich and gorgeous. It was like a flower garden that had no end. It was like a great ocean which was boundless, no matter how far one sailed. It was like the five-colored and seven-colored fabric, whose threads were entangled and could not be unravelled.

If he were not seeking rebirth in the Pure Land, this treasure house could not be exhausted, even if he spent his whole life in it. It would give him the greatest pleasure of study and research.

However, wishing to transcend birth-and-death without any delay, he had to heave a deep sigh, and close the books.

" Your life will last for only ten-odd years." These words constantly rang in Hannen's ears. Then how was he observing the precepts?

He locked himself up in a room for twenty-one days, strictly forbidding others to enter. He sat up straight, cross-legged on the floor, with not even a falling speck of dust to distract him, and only one dim candle-light.

Thus he fasted and concentrated on meditation, but he could not attain the stage of " no-thinking."

Distracting thoughts came one after another. If he tried to drive them away, they came all the more.

Hannen came tottering out of the room, emaciated and bushy-bearded, and could not but wonder whether other performers of austerities were giving false testimony. For the others all behaved as though they had attained enlightenment.

Of course if one meditated for twenty-one days without eating, cut off from the outside world, he could achieve a kind of mental exaltation and a sage-like appearance. But there never could be any consciousness of enlightenment.

Hannen had felt at times during the practices that a strange state of mind had come over him. He had thought this was the state of " no-thinking " and felt great joy. But it was nothing but auto-suggestion which had exalted him temporarily and soon passed away. He could not attain the consciousness, " I have transcended birth-and-death."

No matter how many times he tried, failure resulted just the same.

If the disciplinary practices were performed, not with the aim of attaining enlightenment, but with the desire to increase spiritual power, there would certainly be some effect. But it would not bring about any enlightenment.

Hannen gradually felt the bitterness of disillusion. He began to doubt that other performers were telling the truth. They said they had attained liberation when they had not. It was as if one felt that he had attained liberation when reading some Sutra and being wrapped in the smoke of speculation.

Hannen could not be sure that others were liars. For even if he could not attain liberation through disciplinary practices, he could not say others were the same. Since they said that they were able to attain liberation, he would not dispute them.

Only it was clear to him, at least, that he was not likely to attain liberation.

And there was another thing. As he observed the speech and conduct of those who said they had reached liberation, he felt many doubts.

In this way dark days followed one after another. He gradually exhausted his energy.

He searched all over the mountain for some great monk who could give him a remedy for his agony, but it seemed there was no such person ; because on Mount Hiei, a great monk was either a man of profound Buddhist learning, or a veteran performer of disciplinary practices. Since Hannen had been disappointed in both these types and was seeking for a new light elsewhere, no monk on the mountain could give him anything.

Then what should he do?

He did not know what he should do. There was no way out, it seemed.

What would cure his burning agony then? He could do nothing.

As there was no help, Hannen again had to hunt for Sutras and follow disciplinary practices. But all the more he lost all hope of success.

Such a dark state of mind continued for a long time. His life on the mountain was now becoming a hell on earth.

The temples, Sutra depositories, ceremonial rites,— all began to look like dead bodies. This was exactly like the experience Honen Shonin had gone through. He writes in his book:

" In discipline, I have not accomplished anything. In Zen meditation, I have not accomplished anything. In insight, I have not attained the right wisdom that will destroy passions and give deliverance. Therefore, how could I deliver myself from the bondage of birth-and-death? Regrettable! What shall I do? What shall I do? I am no vessel for the Three Learnings of discipline, meditation, and insight. Are there Buddhist ways, aside from these Three Learnings, that will suit my mind? Or is there a discipline that my body can endure? I seek after wise men and visit scholars, but there is no one who can teach me and no friends who can show me the way. So with heavy heart I enter the Sutra depository and face the sacred Sutras. . . ."

In the world there are people who pretend not to see the real facts of their inward feelings, or who do not like to, and say that their minds are as bright and clear as flawless mirrors. There are also those who are by nature easy-going and nonchalant. These people do not examine themselves strictly because they find it troublesome to do so. They are satisfied with things taken roughly as a whole. And those who are brazen-faced make untrue statements knowingly, and pretend to be wise and virtuous.

But the idealists who are honest and profound and deep in their thinking cannot help examining themselves thoroughly, so they cannot say such easy-going things, much less make pretenses. They cannot, on the other hand, cover up the truth and give false testimony.

It is even so when they suffer inward fears, such as " Without it I cannot be emancipated," or " Without it I cannot get rid of birth-and-death," or " Without it I shall go to hell." For there is no place for false acts.

The uneasiness felt by both Shinran and Honen stems from this point.

It is like a sick person. If his purpose is curing his disease, it will not do at all to conceal his disease. The problem is whether he can be cured or not. If he cannot be cured, he must die. So he looks for efficient doctors and tries remedies. His sickness gradually becomes worse. This unhappiness and frustration suffered by the patient is exactly what Shinran was going through. It was not pretense but a real problem to Shinran.

Zonkaku Shonin[1] writes :

"I try to concentrate my mind but waves of consciousness rise continually; I try to meditate on the moon of ultimate truth, but I cannot, because of the dark clouds."

Kakunyo Shonin[2] also writes :

[1] Son of Kakunyo Shonin.
[2] The third Patriarch of Hongwanji.

" My mind is fretful like the monkey, attracted by worldly things and voices, and enslaved all the more by worldly and intellectual interests."

Shinran, in later years, reminiscently confessed his inward feeling more directly and severely as follows:

" I could not conquer my bad nature; my mind was like the hateful serpent."

Chapter 9

THE ONE-HUNDRED-NIGHT
PILGRIMAGE

Hannen was now in his youthful age of distress.

As time passed, he gradually realized that his nature was centered around human interests rather than on pure intellect. He knew the faith fit for him had to take human interest into consideration. He began to think that it had to be one in which one offers prayers to the Buddha ; rather than an intellectual one, in which one is absorbed in meditation.

It was for this reason that he decided to make a hundred-day visit to the Kannon Bodhisattva at Rokkakudo (Temple).

He was now tired of learning the doctine of the *Lotus Sutra*. His last resort would be to pray to the Kannon Bodhisattva and ask directly for the way of salvation.

The way through the Shirakawa Pass was more level, but as he had decided to go to Rokkakudo and back on foot, he chose the nearer but steeper route which crossed the Shakusan Pass. Even so, the distance was more than eight miles.

The snowy mountain path was cold. The hail splashed on his large hat with cracking sounds. With a book case on his back and a green bamboo stick in hand, he passed the Kirara Slope, which even wood-cutters found difficult to cross, and came near Ichijoji village, as evening came. And when he crossed the Kamo River, the night had already fallen.

When he finally reached Rokkakudo Hall of Chohoji (Temple), his body was as cold as ice. It was already eight o'clock in the evening.

He took off his straw sandals, washed his feet, changed into a monk's white robe, and then prostrated himself before the Nyoirin Kannon[1] Bodhisattva's image.

After a while the sound of the Kei[2] was heard. His life-and-death chanting of the *Lotus Sutra* sounded somewhat like wailing.

" I, Hannen, a Buddha's disciple, stupid by nature, have speculated among the Sutras and meditated in the esoteric hall for twenty years, but have not yet realized the ultimate truth of enlightenment. The path to deliverance appears dim and incomprehensible. I have long lived in delusion and darkness and now know not what to do. If I die thus, I have to fall into hell. Fortunately, being bound to Buddhism by destiny, I became a monk at the age of nine. Ever since I have put my whole heart and soul into Buddhist study, but still I am in a state of darkness. I weep to think that this is due to my past deeds (Karma) and to my stupidity.

[1] Symbol of compassion of the Buddha.
[2] An old stone instrument hung and beaten like a drum,

" O Bodhisattva of great compassion ! Have mercy on me and show me the way to emancipation, fitting for such a dull-witted person as I ! "

Hannen was in tears. He no longer had any pride as a scholar. He only had the one firm determination to be rid of the birth-and-death cycle. He prayed with his whole heart.

He went on praying until he was startled by the bell which rang the hour of four o'clock in the morning. Now he had to go back to the mountain.

The wind blew his black robe as he walked through the Tadasu woods. The snow had become colder with the coming of rain. The steep slope of Kirarazaka was before him.

When he reached Burakuji (Tample), dripping wet, his body and legs were tired out. The priest there offered him some rice-gruel out of pity. At long last Hannen was able to feel comfortable.

Hannen did not fail to visit the Kannon every day, climbing down and up the mountain.

Once a wind-storm caused a landslide which blocked the path, and the rain washed the steep slope in torrents. In spite of this, he stepped into the torrent and completed his trip.

At another time the bridge over the Kamo River was washed away, and he had to wade through. The water of the Kamo River, which had collected the melting snow of the mountains of Hiei and Kurama, was as cold as a sword blade.

" What do I care ! Now this is my last hope," he

thought, and went into the water.

Thus his daily visits continued.

Meanwhile, the snow melted and the water of the Kamo became warmer. When green buds began to come out on the willows on the river banks, his daily visits, too, seemed to have neared a climax.

He had become accustomed to the climb down and up the steep mountain path. He began to feel closer to Kannon's image. At the same time fatigue covered his whole body, and in the hall there was an atmosphere which was neither dream nor reality. Sometimes, sitting in the lamp light, with day and night indistinguishable, he would wonder if he were being held in the arms of the great, compassionate Kannon.

Finally came the completion of his term of worship.

Bracing himself with particular care this night, he purified himself by burning incense, and sat upright chanting the Sutra in front of the Bodhisattva's image.

At about daybreak, he felt something misty and sweet as milk floating toward him, together with a strange smell as of incense, and he fell into a comfortable state of drowsiness, neither waking nor dreaming.

He thought he heard a voice like the spring wind whispering in his ear :

" You may meet with a teacher of the decaying days of the Buddha's Law."

With a start he came to himself.

There was nobody around.

He thought that the voice which was clearly impressed on his mind was surely that of the Kannon.

" You may meet with a teacher of the decaying days of the Buddha's Law," he repeated to himself.

He wondered what fine teacher had been born in the world. He felt this was a sacred omen, and was thankful.

He wanted to meet this great priest without a moment's delay. So thinking, he eagerly waited for the light of day.

Chapter 10

A RARE PERSONAGE

When Hannen left Rokkakudo (Temple) and walked down Higashi-no-toin Street as far as the river bank at Shijo, he saw an elderly man accompanied by an apprentice-boy, and a woman who appeared to be a merchant's wife, walking and talking together. He happened to overhear them say:

" He surely must be a living Buddha ! "

" Certainly. Yoshimizu and thereabouts are filled with worshippers, both priests and laymen. For he teaches the way to rebirth into the Pure Land for all, even to us tradesmen, without any discrimination."

" He does not look down upon women, but says that they too can become Buddhas. No learning is necessary, only recitation of the Nembutsu, and the Amida will deliver us, he says. How thankful I am ! I shall be saved at last ! This is exactly like rainfall that ends a drought."

" It's the deliverance by the great compassionate Amida, which no great priests have ever revealed to us."

" We really were lucky to have been born at this time ! "

" The whole town of Kyoto is talking about it. I hear that those outside of town have heard of it, too, and everyone has begun to recite the Nembutsu. What a blessed thing it is ! "

" Master, can even I be saved if I recite the Nembutsu ? " asked the apprentice-boy.

" Yes, of course. You can be reborn into the Pure Land, too, if you recite the Nembutsu. So recite it with a whole heart."

" What a wonderful thing it would be, if the whole city and outskirts, everywhere, were filled with the recitation of the Nembutsu ! "

" Then there wouldn't be any thieves in town, would there ? "

" No. For even thieves can be saved if they recite the Nembutsu, I hear."

Hannen listened with attentive ears. His heart beat fast.

" Honen Shonin is the living Buddha of these days. All go to Yoshimizu. All go to Yoshimizu."

The three walked away, talking.

Hannen stood for a while.

" ' You may meet with a teacher of the decaying days of the Buddha's Law.' Yes, this is it," he said to himself, hitting his knee.

" If one recites the Buddha's name, he, whether he is an old man, or a woman, or an apprentice-boy, or even a thief, can be saved. . . . He surely is no ordinary man who says this. He certainly must be the teacher of the latter days of Buddhism."

He began to walk with quick steps.

" But . . . " he stopped to think. "Am I, who was briefly Abbot of the Emperor-patronized Shokoin (Temple), and who have studied on the mountain for twenty years, to recite the Buddha's name on the same level with illiterate people such as the apprentice-boy and the merchant's wife? "

" Silly ! " he then sneered at himself. " I have nothing. I haven't grasped anything, not even a piece of straw, that will help me to attain enlightenment. I have nothing ! I'm truly a mendicant ! "

He quickened his pace toward Higashiyama.

When he reached Yoshimizu Zenbo (Temple) and introduced himself, he was taken to a special room without delay.

Honen Shonin was sixty-five years old. He and Hannen were like father and son in respect to age. His gentle look with fathomless dignity in its warmth having matured with the years, had an effect like mild spring weather on the visitor sitting opposite him.

Hannen explained to him in detail the course of his search after Truth, and asked him for the way to deliver himself from birth-and-death without recourse to learning the Sutra or practicing discipline.

Honen Shonin listened to Hannen with his eyes closed, and then he said :

" Your course exactly mirrors the path I have taken. I went to Mount Hiei when I was fifteen, and for thirty years after that, I underwent all the discipline and practices of the Holy Path (Shodo). I read all the sacred books of the great collection five times over. I practiced the Perfect precepts of Mahayana (Endonkai), and esoteric meditation. There is not a practice that I have not performed. Furthermore, I pursued my studies in the southern city of Nara, and called on great teachers at Daigo and Omuro. I made difficult studies and practiced austerities until I became forty. But still I was not able to free myself from the enslavement of birth-and-death.

" Then I happened to read Zendo's[1] book called *Sanzengi*,[2] which said :

'Recite the Buddha's Name with a whole heart, walking or lying, no matter for how long or short a time. One who continues to do this moment by moment is rightly established to be reborn into the Pure Land because it is in accordance with the Buddha's Vow. '

" Then with a sudden flash the truth burst upon me.

" The significant point is ' because it is in accordance with the Buddha's Vow.'

" It is not because of the merits of our own practices. Our rebirth into the Pure Land is due to the power of the Buddha's earnest Vow to deliver us. We need not worry, even if our intelligence is low and our practices are crude.

---

[1] Zendo (613–681) was a great Chinese advocate of the Pure Land doctrine.

[2] Commentary on the *Kanmuryojukyo*.

" For we are not going to be delivered because of the merits of these things, but solely because of the great Eighteenth Vow of the Bhikku Dharmakara, who said that if he could not deliver us dull-witted people, he would not become a Buddha. And he did become a Buddha, and so our rebirth into the Pure Land is certain.

" Nothing can be more certain. There is nothing else we can add. It is because ' it is in accordance with the Buddha's Vow. ' "

Hannen felt as if a thousand claps of thunder had tolled. A great shock like the Six Great Earthquakes penetrated his body and soul.

He had nothing to say. He had wondered what fabulous reasons made it possible for apprentice-boys and thieves to be reborn into the Pure Land. But, this, indeed, was an unimaginable great principle, something that could not come out of the human mind. It was transcendent truth that could only come out of the Buddha's wisdom.

His ears had never heard such a great truth since he was born. No mortal philosopher could originate a great thought such as this !

This was totally the Buddha's way of thinking. It is His Law, the knowledge that came radiating from the ' Other Side,' from the Pure Land.

Hannen was so surprised and was so overwhelmed with thankfulness that he could not utter a word. He only wept large tears on the mat.

But Honen Shonin understood Hannen's mind very clearly.

Hannen realized that he had become as composed as a rock. He felt security, freedom, and self-effacement at the same time, which required nothing from him.

Perhaps this was what we call the " instant enlightenment."

Generally speaking, the most difficult part of faith is to cast away everything you possess. When you have cast it away, enlightenment is at your feet. But the possessions which you cast away must be things that are worth more than anything else in the world to you.

To Hannen, his learning, discipline and practices had been his pride and life. They had been the things which had made his life worth living on the mountain.

But since hearing Prince Shotoku's words in the dream about the end of his life, he realized that his possessions would not help in any way to attain rebirth in the Pure Land. The things which till then had been his hope and pride became useless to him. He no longer possessed anything. The egg had matured, and had only to wait for the mother bird to peck at it with its bill.

At this moment an altogether different, magnificent Law was revealed to him, and he was instantly enlightened.

He was at last able to understand the Prince's words. " Your life will last for only ten-odd years " had meant that his life of self-efforts on the Sages' Path on the mountain would last for ten years.

And the Prince's words, "As soon as your life ends, you will be reborn into the Pure Land," had meant that as soon as his life of self-effort ended, he would enter the Pure Land School of instant enlightenment and " Easy Practice."[1]

Hannen understood clearly that his relation to the life on the mountain had been severed.

Considering the dream prophecy and the nature of his faith, Hannen thought it was now time to leave the mountain.

Until his rebirth into the Pure Land was rightly established, he had hated the life on the mountain. But now he did not have any such feeling.

He was now prepared to leave the mountain with a feeling of gratitude toward his teachers, and friends, and nature, and everything else on the mountain that had nurtured him for twenty years, readying him to have his eye of faith opened.

Hannen went back to the mountain and spent the day quietly in his quarters in the Shokoin (Temple), putting all his things in order so that he might not inconvenience anybody. And he had a friendly farewell talk with young monks and pages. Such composure of mind had been entirely impossible for him until the day before.

The following day he sent a letter of farewell to the administration office in Hodoin (Temple).

Teachers and friends were all sorry that Hannen was leaving. Many were sorry to see him become a common priest in a black robe, for honors were open to him

[1] Attainment of enlightenment by accepting Amida Buddha's compassion.

in the near future, Abbot Jichin having become the 66th abbot of the Head Temple. But they were unable to stop him, seeing that his resolution was firm.

Hannen, too, was full of deep emotion when the time finally came for him to descend from the mountain. It was especially sad for him to leave the Abbot, who had been kind and affectionate to him ever since he had taken the ordination rites.

Hannen formally rode in an ox-carriage in departing from Shokoin (Temple). He had the children and the footmen in the Buddhist procession wear new ceremonial clothes. He, too, wore a white robe.

The unforgettable Seminary of Three Pagodas and Sixteen Valleys, farewell! The peak of Shimei and the grove of Shakusan, farewell!

Hannen departed from the mountain, frequently looking back as the carriage moved at the slow pace of the bull.

Chapter 11

ENLIGHTENMENT BY FAITH AND
ENLIGHTENMENT BY PRACTICE

In his first interview with Honen Shonin, Hannen abandoned his ambition for self-realization, which he had cherished for twenty years, and turned to the sole practice of the Nembutsu. This upright attitude of Hannen was precisely in accord with Honen's desires.

Hannen's ardent spirit made Honen recall the Chinese master, Doshaku Zenji. Thereupon Honen gave Hannen the Buddhist name Shakku, of which the last syllable ' ku ' was taken from his own name Genku.

Hannen was Shakku from then on. With the change of his name, he cast away his official rank and became a common priest in black hemp robe. Completely abandoning the goal of self-realization, he became a follower of the ' Other Power ' of the Jodo Sect, one of those who recite the Nembtusu day and night.

Shakku built himself a hut in the village of Okazaki, at the foot of Kaguragaoka (hill). His abode was not far from Yoshimizu. Every morning and evening he walked to Yoshimizu, rounding the back of Kachozan hill.

From his abode he could easily see the tiled roof of Shorenin (Temple) where his black hair had been tonsured for the first time.

His greatest pleasure was to hear the sermons preached by Honen, who was like an affectionate father. Shakku felt that Honen was a fine teacher. Honen Shonin trusted Shakku more and more. The friendship between teacher and pupil continued to grow.

Honen Shonin was a great, learned sage of many virtues. No matter what sort of problem was placed before him, a solution was always in his power.

His convictions and ideas matured with old age, until there was not even a tiny opening for criticism.

The Shonin himself was calm, broad-minded, and absolutely free from affectation. Most people appeared child-like in his presence, due to his greater knowledge, mental powers and maturity.

Shakku often compared himself to Honen Shonin. He thought that the teacher was born more versatile and peaceful, and superior in Karmic virtues, as if born under a gentle, favorable star. On the other hand, Shakku felt his own nature was undisciplined, full of frustrations, and inferior in Karmic virtues.

For example, it was unthinkable that Honen Shonin would ever wail. But, he himself would likely wail and lament. He could not imagine his teacher's mind and body worn out by delusions and afflictions. Even if an adverse wind should rage, Honen would calmly steer through all difficulties, as if sailing before the wind.

But Shakku felt there would be all kinds of stormy disturbances in his own lifetime. It seemed unlikely that he could live a peaceful and harmonious life.

But there was no difference between him and his teacher in one respect : both were going to be delivered by reciting the Nembutsu. This was indeed reassuring and gratifying.

A great many followers always gathered at Yoshimizu Zenbo (Temple), and the voices reciting the Nembutsu resounded both within and without the temple.

Some of these followers had been Imperial guards, before they entered the priesthood. Some had been monks of the Tendai Sect of Mount Hiei, or the Shingon Sect of Nara, before they were converted to the Nembutsu School. They came from various backgrounds, and the home pupils alone numbered several hundred.

As in all religious training however, many followers were unworthy of their master. Not all of the disciples were following Honen Shonin's teaching and had attained adamant faith in regard to their rebirth into the Pure Land.

On this day, about two hundred disciples had gathered at Yoshimizu Zenbo. The hall was divided into three sections, the left, the right, and the middle. Honen Shonin, the teacher, was seated in front of the middle section. By his side sat Shakku, acting as secretary.

The followers remained standing, and looked at each other, wondering what to expect.

Shakku then broke the silence. He said :

" You may be wondering what we are to do. Today

we are to be separated into the two sections of
"Shin-futai" (enlightenment by faith), and "Gyo-futai"
(enlightenment by the Nembutsu practice). Is our rebirth into the Pure Land established by our faith, or by
our Nembutsu practice? Please be seated on either
side, according to your understanding."

All the people stood still and quiet for some time.

After a while, Shokaku Hoin and Horen-bo nodded
to others and sat in the seats belonging to Shin-futai.

Secretary Shakku took down their names.

Just then Kumagai Rensho-bo came in late. He
looked at the people and inquired in a loud voice,
" Secretary Shakku, what is all this? "

" Today we are to choose between Shin-futai and
Gyo-futai. We are to decide whether our rebirth into
the Pure Land is established through our faith, or
through our Nembutsu practice."

Rensho-bo nodded, and without any hesitation, took
a seat on the side of Shin-futai.

The secretary immediately wrote his name down.
He waited for others to follow, but they only looked at
each other and hesitated.

Thereupon Shakku put down his brush and took a
seat belonging to the side of Shin-futai.

Finally Honen Shonin quietly took a seat on the same
side.

This showed that those who had embraced positive
faith were surprisingly few. However, there was a
reason why many followers hesitated to sit on the side
of Shin-futai, It was because Honen Shonin's practices

were so firm and his personality was so noble, that he put his heart and soul into the repetition of the Nembutsu.

In general, the difference between the Jodo Sect and the Shin Sect at present is this : the Gyo-futai aspect of the Judo School became the Jodo Sect, and the Shin-futai aspect of the Jodo School became the Shin Sect. The two sects came out of the same Jodo school, and the two aspects were definitely found in Honen Shonin's Nembutsu practice. It was later with the rise of Shinran Shonin that the Gyo-futai aspect was cleared away, and the sole merit of Shin-futai was upheld.

Therefore, when he followers saw Honen Shonin sit on the side of Shin-futai, some of them looked embarrassed, and others looked discontented.

At present, when books such as *Ichimai Kishomon*,[1] *Senjakushu*[2], and *Tannisho*[3] are available, we who have read them, may think that Honen Shonin's followers were ignorant. But in those days the books were not available. These followers had seen their teacher Honen's devotion to discipline, his daily behavior, his assiduous repetition of the Nembutsu for tens of thousands of times. So it was not surprising that they should hesitate when tested all of a sudden, even if they had learned the fundamental principle of " rebirth into the Pure Land by the ' Other Power.' "

Kumagai Rensho-bo and Shakku did not hesitate for

[1] Essence of *Senjakushu*.

[2] The system of Honen's Jodo doctrine.

[3] Written by Yuien-bo, Shinran's follower.

the same reason that they embraced the Buddhist faith —the realization that no practices were adequate. Honen Shonin himself had gone through the same experience.

That day even the amiable Shonin was disappointed. This thing must have struck him with intense surprise, for he had been absorbed in thought.

Shakku had no idea that this event was destined to bring about a very great change in his life.

Chapter 12

THE PROPHECY ABOUT A BEAUTIFUL WOMAN

Shakku had a strange dream again.

He had received guidance in his dreams at critical moments in his life, and so he regarded them reverently and attentively.

This dream was about the Nyoirin Kannon Bodhisattva of the Rokkakudo Temple, where he had made daily visits for one hundred nights, and by whose (Bodhisattva's) guidance he had been introduced to Honen Shonin.

The instructions were most awe-inspiring and amazing.

In the dream the Kannon Bodhisattva said:

" Reverend, if you are destined by your former Karma to come in contact with a woman, I shall become a beautiful woman and be your wife. I shall make an ideal home all my life, and in my last moments shall guide you to the Land of Bliss."

Had anyone received such an awesome prophecy before?

The Kannon went on:

" This is my vow.   Explain the meaning of this vow, and let all living creatures hear it."

Shakku then saw rugged mountains soaring high on the eastern side of the temple, and an assembly of beings between these mountains.

When he awoke he was wet with perspiration.   His fast-beating heart was filled with emotions—perplexity, pride, gratitude, awe.

The Buddha's words were indeed awe-inspiring.

After all, his life was in the hands of the Buddha, but why should such unprecedented omens be revealed to him, who had already become a priest?   Why had he been chosen to undergo such a trial?

Shakku kept all this to himself, and did not say a thing about it to anyone, not even to his teacher. Though he continued his work at Yoshimizu Zenbo, he lost his usual presence of mind.   Whenever he recalled the dream, he felt a great uneasiness.

Lord Tsukinowa Kanezane was a lay disciple who had close spiritual ties with Honen Shonin.   He had resigned from his office of regent, and was now leading a retired life at Tsukinowa Hill.   He spent days reciting the Nembutsu with his whole heart.   He was not only eager to learn Buddhism, but also to ask questions.

One day he called at Yoshimizu Zenbo and asked Honen Shonin the following questions :

" Though a layman, born in the latter days of Buddhism, I have been able to meet with the truth of the ' Other Power, ' and this gives me great delight.   But those around Shonin are all priests following strict discipline and precepts. More than two hundred of these priests are practicing purity.   On the other hand, I am a layman, eating meat, being married, and not keeping the Five Precepts.   I believe, therefore, the Nembutsu which the priests recite and the Nembutsu which I recite cannot have the same merits.   This idea worries me."

Shonin answered earnestly :

" This is a question which a right-minded layman always asks.   But it does not pierce the core of the ' Other Power.'   As I always say, the rebirth into the Pure Land by the ' Other Power ' is not due to our past merits.   It is all due to the power of the Buddha's Vow. Therefore, there is no difference between the Nembutsu recited by priests and the Nembutsu recited by laymen. There is no need for such misgivings."

" Then in the faith by the ' Other Power,' is there no difference between keeping the precepts and breaking the precepts ? "

" No, there is no difference."

" That makes me feel at ease.   Till now, I had no questions about the teaching, but I had doubts about the laymen's capacities."

" It is quite natural for you to have such doubts.   To tell the truth, even among the priests who are pupils of this temple, there are a number who have the same doubts.   It is human nature to become perplexed."

Lord Kanezane considered this thoughtfully and then said :

" That makes me believe that all people in generations

to come will surely suffer from the same doubts. Especially after Shonin is gone, this question may hinder the spreading of the great teaching.

" Since concrete examples are the best authority, will you please select a follower who firmly believes in salvation through the ' Other Power,' and give him to me? Fortunately, I have a daughter who is still unmarried, and I would like to have her marry such a follower. Then there would be proof, in all the ages to come, that one can be reborn into the Pure Land, whether one is a priest or a layman, a man or a woman, an ordinary mortal or a sage. Such an advantage would be enormous. What does my venerable teacher think about it?"

Lord Kanezane's face showed his firm resolution.

The followers present all held their breath and strained their ears to hear what the Shonin would say in reply.

The brilliant teacher Honen Shonin clearly perceived the delicate situation. His answer would greatly influence the entire future of the sect that advocated salvation by the ' Other Power.' If he should retreat a single step now, the religion of salvation by the ' Other power ' would be forever weakened.

" That is a splendid idea," said Honen, not at all excited. " Shakku, you had better do as the Lord tells you to do."

Those present were startled. They looked at the Shonin, and then at Shakku.

Shakku turned pale. He said:

" Ever since I became a follower, I have wished to

follow all my teacher's instructions.   But this command
seems impossible to accept.   Since my ordination I have
been negligent sometimes, but not where women are
concerned.   Why should I associate with a woman
now?"

"No, I am not persuading you to marry because you
are in love or anything like that, but because this is an
expedient means of spreading the great Law."

"Even if that be so, why must I be chosen from the
great number of your followers?"

"Shakku . . ." Honen Shonin's kind, dignified face
commanded respect.   "This is due to your past Karma.
Think it over."

Shakku was startled, for he recalled the prophetic
dream of the Kannon—"I shall become a beautiful
woman and be your wife."

Even so, how did the Shonin know of this?   Shakku
had heard that the Shonin had supernatural powers.

Once he had accompanied the Shonin to Lord Tsukinowa's residence.   A room had been specially prepared for the Shonin because of his great age.   There
Shakku was waiting, while the Shonin was having a
religious discourse with Kanezane in the inner room.

It was autumn, and in the garden red leaves were lit
by the soft glow of the setting sun.

Just then, the beautiful daughter of the Lord hurriedly
emerged from the hedge, as if she were excited or upset.
She fell on the ground and worshipped.   Her maid-
servants hastily followed her.

"Princess, what is the matter?"

" Just now the Shonin stepped on the lotus and walked in the air. Didn't you see it? "

The waiting-women looked at each other and said, " No, we didn't see anything."

" But I certainly saw him. It was a most uplifting sight." So saying, she gazed at the place where she had seen the vision. But then she suddenly noticed Shakku watching. She blushed, and with a bow departed with her maids.

The sight of the beautiful girl who worshipped the vision among the autumn red leaves was deeply impressed on Shakku's mind.

When Shakku later told the Shonin about the vision, the latter seemed unconcerned. " Perhaps such a thing may be possible. Don't say anything about it to others," he said.

Now Shakku recalled the happenings of that day. He felt that the Shonin knew about the prophecy through some supernatural power.

Shakku thought he could no longer escape his fate.

The Shonin looked at Shakku and said encouragingly, " Be a martyr to the propagation of the great Law. You have nothing to fear. Because of this marriage, you may have to face all kinds of insults and misfortunes. But they will help to spread the great Law. They will help to bring many millions of people into contact with Buddhism. Be a martyr willingly for the Law. I assign you this mission, because I have had an eye on you as a Nembutsu devotee of great courage."

Shakku could not help obeying his teacher's orders.

At the Lord's villa at Gojo Nishi-no-toin, the unprecedented marriage ceremony was performed. The bride was Tamahi, the youngest daughter of Lord Tsukinowa Kanezane. She was eighteen years old. The groom was Shakku, a common priest in black robe, a disciple of Honen Shonin. He was thirty-one.

Fish and fowl were served at the wedding ceremony. And before the decoration of mandarin ducks, the two were united as man and wife.

Nothing could harm the Nembutsu. The Nembutsu would shine far and wide, transcending all things both pure and impure.

It was nothing but man's subjectivity that feared meat and matrimony.

Chapter 13

BEFORE THE STORM

Needless to say, the story of this marriage spread rapidly from mouth to mouth in the streets of Kyoto.

"I hear a follower of the Buddha has taken a wife."

"Honen Shonin was the match-maker, they say."

There were some who laughed with cynical scorn.

"I hope he will not be more attracted by his wife than by the Buddha."

"If one can be born in the Land of Bliss in this way, there will no longer be priests who are unmarried, will there?"

"Don't talk nonsense. They have given an example to the people that both priests and laymen alike can be reborn into the Pure Land through the Nembutsu."

"You're right, you're right. Shakku is really great, for he took the initiative in eating meat and getting married, knowing very well that he would be abused."

Some praising and some condemning, none of the people was free of the Buddha's influence.

The Nembutsu Sect was riding on a wave of popularity. In all the streets of Kyoto, the subject of talk among the people, both high and low, rich and poor, was the Nembutsu Sect.

At Yoshimizu Temple there was a constant stream of visitors. The unbroken line of people going and coming stretched a curtain, as it were, with their wide sleeves, and the recitation of the Nembutsu echoed both in and out of the temple.

How could the bombastic monks on Mount Hiei overlook this? From the very first, they had feared neither the military clans nor the Imperial Court. The monks said:

" They preach the Easy Path of the ' Other Power, ' neglecting discipline, and regarding us followers of the Sage's Path of self-effort with enmity. And they are deceiving the public. That is bad enough. But how dumbfounding for a priest to get married ! This offense against the Buddhist precepts is a disgrace, and will surely make Buddhist dignity fall to the ground.

" Those who have studied on Mount Hiei and have strictly followed the Buddhist precepts are being converted to the Nembutsu Sect in rapid succession. Not only that, they all condemn the Sage's Path of self-power. This is outrageous !

" If we do not uproot this heresy, Buddhism will finally be replaced by paganism. It's time to draw the sword and fight for the traditions of Mount Hiei ! "

The large bell of the Great Lecture Hall was rung, and three thousand monks assembled with angry eyes.

They immediately passed a resolution. They sent appeals in all directions, and petitioned the Abbot of the Head Temple to stop the Nembutsu practice.

The petition by the mountain monks meant an appeal by force, carrying the portable shrine of the mountain god through the streets of Kyoto for a demonstration against the Imperial Court.

Under such conditions, it was Tsukinowa Kanezane who exerted himself most. He undertook mediation between Mount Hiei and Yoshimizu, and busied himself to nullify the monks' appeal to the Court. This effort continued all his life.

It was due to Lord Kanezane's successful mediation that in the first year of Genkyu,[1] the Nembutsu Sect drafted the seven-article oath with the joint signatures of one hundred ninety elders, and submitted it to the Abbot of Mount Hiei, and narrowly managed to relieve the crisis.

But this was only a temporary calm. The situation was such that a heavy storm was bound to come. All thoughtful people perceived this and grieved.

Among the followers of Honen Shonin who had been receiving direct instruction were Anraku-bo and Juren-bo. They had formerly been Imperial guards, but they aspired after salvation and became believers in the Nembutsu, and entered the priesthood. They were enjoying the teaching of Honen Shonin.

Their temple at Shishigatani flourished more and more with the prosperity of the Nembutsu Sect. It was located at the outskirts of the capital. The hill was beautiful, the water was clear, and it was a fine place for a temple.

[1] 1206 A. D.

Moreover, the enthusiasm of the two priests, and the beautiful voices with which they chanted the Nembutsu gradually won over the people who visited the temple. The special Nembutsu sessions which they held became especially popular among the people, old and young, men and women. They expanded and rebuilt the temple to accommodate several hundred worshippers. It became a respectable temple, a leading one among the Nembutsu Sect.

At the Bon festival[1] held on July 15 in the first year of Ken-ei,[2] this Anrakuji (Temple) invited Honen Shonin to hold a special Nembutsu session. The news spread all over the capital, and the number of visitors was enormous.

One day two beautiful women's palanquins hurried toward Shishigatani, passing along the foot of Higashi-yama. The palanquins stopped in front of the gate of Anrakuji.

Two court-ladies appeared, wearing veils dyed with the juice of autumn grass. They mingled with the crowd, trying to avoid notice, and entered the temple. They sat in a corner, as if hiding themselves, and listened to the sermon.

Honen Shonin was at that moment preaching about the origin of *Shukke Kudoku Sutra :*

" While Sakyamuni Buddha was still alive, there was in India a rich man's wife named Kurana. She was living in great luxury. Once she heard a sermon by the

[1] Ullambana in Sanskrit, the Festival of the Dead.

[2] 1206 A.D. The name of the era was changed to Ken-ei on April 27.

honorable Kaladayin, and began to long for salvation. When her husband was far away to trade, she took away her hair-ornaments and became a nun. Meanwhile her husband came back from his trip to Persia and Arabia, with a great many precious stones and spices which he had bought, and heard that his wife had become a nun. He was enraged. He caught her and put her in jail and waited for her hair to grow. Then he made her return to secular life.

"When she died she went to a burning hell. But by dint of her good merit of once having been a nun, she was saved and was able to be born in the celestial world."

Here the first part of the sermon ended and there was an intermission.

The two court-ladies seemed to have been inspired greatly by the sermon. But they apparently had come here secretly and could not stay long, for they left the temple, and hurried away in the palanquins.

If the two ladies had heard the second part of the sermon, their fate might have taken a different course.

After this they came to the temple from time to time.

Soon people were saying, "They are the court-ladies, Matsumushi and Suzumushi."

"They are the most charming court-ladies at the Palace, they say, and are called the beauties of the Sento Palace."

"Those two are the only favorites of the ex-Emperor."

It was natural that they caught the worshippers' attention. Though there were many women worshippers at this temple, these two were especially refined, beautiful, and elegantly dressed.

Days and months passed by.

On December 26 at midnight, there was the sound of knocking at the door of Anrakuji (Temple). At first they thought it might be the wind, but it was not.

When Anraku-bo opened the door suspiciously, the two well-remembered court-ladies came running in.

" I'm sorry to have disturbed you in the dead of night," said one of them. " I am a lady-in-waiting called Matsumushi, serving at the Sento Palace. And this is . . ."

" Suzumushi, in the same service," said the other.

"And for what reason did the court-ladies . . .? "

" That is because we want very much to renounce the world, and so we stole out of the Palace. Please perform the ordination rites for us this very night."

Anraku-bo was struck with surprise. He showed them into the temple. But he could not deal with the matter himself, so he went to call Juren-bo.

" It is praiseworthy that you should want to renounce the world," said Juren-bo. " But in the Nembutsu Sect, faith does not necessarily go with supra-worldly discipline. It is best for you to utter the Nembutsu while living at the Palace."

" No, no," said Matsumushi. " We have made a firm resolution. We are eager to become nuns and serve the Buddha day and night."

Once Matsumushi had made up her mind, it seemed nothing could dissuade her.

Suzumushi, too, said tearfully, " Since we have set

our minds on renouncing the world, we have been apt to neglect our court services. And because that is wrong, we thought we would exchange court service for the Buddha's service. We think that in this way we can make real repayment. So won't you arrange for the ordination rites quickly, please?"

Juren-bo, too, was at a loss. "But there is a certain procedure to be followed in the ordination. Since it would be imprudent to perform it at night like this, will you return to the Palace for a while? It would be possible for you to be ordained after you have asked for leave, and after I have told my teacher, the Shonin, about it."

Matsumushi and Suzumushi exchanged looks of embarrassment.

"We have sneaked away from the Palace, never to return, so we cannot go back for any reason," said one of them.

"We had asked for leave but were refused, so we were compelled to steal out of the Palace. We no longer want to do court service. Won't you please take pity on us and ordain us?"

The two ladies knelt down and worshipped, begging to be ordained. Both Anraku-bo and Juren-bo stood there at a loss, for though they sympathized with the two ladies, they feared trouble might follow.

"Is tonsuring impossible, despite all our begging?"

"Are you priests so afraid of the authorities that you shrink from giving us the ordination?"

The two ladies looked up at the priests reproachfully.

Their eyes, beautiful with tears, showed the determination of women who were no longer afraid of anything.

" Though we feel pity for you, until the ex-Emperor returns from Kumano . . ." Anraku-bo began, when the ladies exchanged glances.

" Suzumushi, now that . . ."

" Yes, Matsumushi, as there is no hope of our returning to the Palace, let's once and for all . . ."

Daggers glittered. Holding the handle wrapped in her sleeve of figured silk, each lady was about to plunge the dagger into her throat.

" Please wait," Juren-bo hastily stopped them. And to Anraku-bo he said, "Anraku-bo, these two ladies have made such a great resolution. If we do not save them, being afraid of censure, it means that we priests would be committing a sin."

" That's right, Juren-bo. We were both formerly Hokumen guards of the ex-Emperor. It would be a disgrace for all generations, if people said we neglected the Buddha's Law because we were afraid of losing our lives."

"A Sutra says, ' If one in a family enters the priesthood, nine will be born in the celestial world.' No matter what may happen afterwards, let us guide the two souls to the celestial world."

" Then you will grant our request to take the tonsure? "

" Certainly. We shall perform the ordination rites in deference to your firm determination."

" Thank you very much. Oh, let us praise the

Buddha ! " The two court-ladies knelt and worshipped,
looking most delighted.

"And after you have taken the tonsure, where will
you escape? If you remain here, you will face huge
difficulties."

"As for that matter, I know of someone in my home
town of Kokawa, in the province of Kii, so I think
we'll go there for the present."

" That will be fine."

In the meantime daybreak gradually neared.

The two priests worshipped before the altar, and had
the two court-ladies seated side by side. Then the
priests shaved off all their beautifully ornamented hair.

To regret the end of beauty is a feeling of common
mortals only. The two nuns were in an ecstasy of joy.
They cast off their garments, and put on coarse black
robes. Matsumushi received the new Buddhist name
Myotei-ni ; and Suzumushi, that of Myochi-ni. Then
with bamboo sticks and braided hats in hand, they
secretly set out for Kii, before the new day dawned.

Chapter 14

THE PROHIBITION OF THE NEMBUTSU RECITATION

The ex-Emperor returned from his trip to Kumano on the 16th of January. Having spent lonely nights on his journey, viewing the desolate mountain scenery of Mikumano and the rustic shores of Waka-no-ura, he had been longing for warm, feminine charms.

His disappointment was great when he came back to his Sento Palace and found that his two court-ladies, who had been his comfort morning and evening, had gone.

The ladies in charge of the palace were seized with panic. At first they tried to smooth over the incident, but finally it became clear that the two ladies had secretly left the palace on the night of December 16, and that their whereabouts were unknown.

A strict investigation began. The Police and Judicial Office reported that there were indications that the two ladies had become believers in the Nembutsu School of Buddhism, advocated by Honen Shonin, and that, being extremely weary of life, they had become nuns. The ex-Emperor burst into a rage.

Someone secretly informed Mount Hiei, and it became known among the monks. They rejoiced at this, thinking there would be no better opportunity to protest. They sent a written appeal to Kofukuji (Temple) in Nara, and it was arranged that Mount Hiei would co-operate with Kofukuji in the movement.

They began a strong demonstration against the government, and proclaimed:

> We demand that the Nembutsu School be closed. If a law is not immediately enacted, both Buddhism and the Emperor's Laws will fall to the ground, and the world will be in darkness, resulting in serious disturbances.
>
> "Some time ago the followers of Yoshimizu Temple submitted a written apology signed by the elders and also a written pledge, but thereafter there have been no indications that the Nembutsu followers have reformed their practices. On the contrary, they are offending the Buddhist commandments and committing disgraceful acts. It is outrageous how they disregard Buddhist Laws and scorn the Laws of the Emperor.
>
> "If our appeal is not accepted, we fear what the gods of Mount Hiei and of the Kasuga Shrine, who protect Buddhism, would decree."

Tsukinowa Kanezane and other sympathizers of Yoshimizu were this time at a loss to make peace, for now the ex-Emperor himself was greatly angered.

Finally an Imperial Order was issued to prohibit the recitation of the Nembutsu. Imposing notice-boards were put up at crossroads, in and around the city of Kyoto, saying:

"The recitation of the Nembutsu is strictly forbidden, not even a single utterance. In witness whereof we set our seals hereunto."

The monks on Mount Hiei and in Nara rejoiced with an "I-told-you-so" air.

On the other hand, men and women ceased to visit Yoshimizu Zenbo (Temple), and the place was utterly deserted. But Honen Shonin looked just as usual, and did not seem to be surprised or grieved. His expression proclaimed that this was a common occurrence. His attitude was that of merely watching worldly affairs that would go on repeating themselves. He seemed to say:

"Look at the rise and fall of the people in the last twenty years. The Heikes declined, and so did Kiso Yoshinaka. The Genjis, too, are on their way to a downfall. As we have seen them rise and fall, we should not forget that this matter now at hand should also be faced calmly. Of course this time we have to stand in the midst of the disaster. However, these mortal lives of ours are always afloat on the waves blown by the wind of our past doings (Karma), and there is nothing new about them."

" ' I may lose my life tomorrow according to my past Karma '—isn't this what all the followers of the Nembutsu should always be prepared for?"

Honen Shonin was neither excited nor dispirited, but continued with his daily task of reciting the Nembutsu for seventy thousand times.   As there were no worshippers now coming to Yoshimizu, the Shonin would sometimes recite in a loud voice.

His followers were worried, saying:

" Since the Nembutsu is prohibited, won't you please be careful not to recite it aloud? "

The Shonin did not try to argue; nevertheless, he did not show signs of flinching.

Lord Tsukinowa was concerned about this, fearing something might happen to the Shonin.   So he asked the Shonin to close the Yoshimizu Temple, which attracted too much attention from other sects and schools, and to move to quarters at Hoshoji (Temple).   The Shonin did as he was asked.

The investigation by the Police and Judicial Office finally revealed that Anraku-bo and Juren-bo had ordained Matsumushi and Suzumushi and helped them to flee.

Juren-bo gave himself up to the authorities.   The supreme court at Nishihachijo put him immediately into the west prison of the Imperial Guards.

Hearing this, Anraku-bo too decided to give himself up.   But if he went to prison, he might never see his teacher, the Shonin, again.   So he visited Honen Shonin at Hoshoji (Temple) in order to apologize for his role in the present calamity.

Anraku-bo prostrated himself before the Shonin, saying:

" My thoughtlessness has brought about this great calamity on the Nembutsu School.   I do not know how to apologize to you for it.   I am afraid what retribution this might bring."

The Shonin smiled as usual and said,

" The Buddha always shines like the sun.   Only at times there are clouds and mists that obscure him. Even if there is a severe thunderstorm for a while, it is bound to become bright in the course of time ; for it is natural for the sun to shine.   Do not worry.   Only do not neglect to recite the Nembutsu."

" I am prepared for the punishment, which I deserve," said Anraku-bo.   " But I cannot sleep when I think that the Shonin might be blamed without cause."

" If I should meet with misfortune in the cause of the Nembutsu, the martyrdom would be a matter of great satisfaction to me.   The Nembutsu followers will all be reborn into the Pure Land and live on the same lotus petals.   Never have any fears."

Anraku-bo's tears fell as he said, " Having received your gracious words, I, Anraku-bo, have nothing to repent, even if I am condemned to capital punishment."

He left the temple in high spirits and walked toward the palace at Gojo, in order to give himself up to the authorities.   In front of the Yomei Gate of the palace he saw a notice-board prohibiting the Nembutsu, and some police officials sitting nearby with a group of soldiers.

Seeing this, Anraku-bo burned with indignation, and he recited loudly :

" King Cakravarti was high in rank,

But his seven treasures did not last long.
Though his heavenly abode was filled with joy,
The five weaknesses soon showed themselves.
Namu-Amida-Butsu, Namu-Amida-Butsu."

" You scoundrel ! Such a loud recitation of the Nembutsu near the palace ! Catch him, all of you ! " said an official.

The soldiers jumped upon Anraku-bo and bound him.

When it became known that he was the leader that aided the court-ladies, the officials' rage was even greater.

On the 9th of February, Anraku-bo and Juren-bo faced public trial, and after the examination of their crime by court-nobles, both were condemned to death.

After that, state councilors were summoned. They made inquiries into the crimes of Honen-bo and his leading disciples at Yoshimizu.

As a result, Honen-bo was sentenced to be exiled to the province of Tosa, Jomon-bo to Bingo, and Zenko-bo to Hoki. Other leading disciples were all exiled to various provinces. Besides the death penalty decreed for Anraku-bo and Juren-bo, some wanted Shakku-bo to be sentenced to death, for eating meat and marrying. But Rokkaku Chunagon Chikatsune, one of the councilors, protested against this ; Shakku narrowly escaped death, but was sentenced to be exiled to the province of Echigo. Due to the friendly influence of Tsukinowa Kanezane, Honen-bo's place of exile was changed to the province of Sanuki.

Anraku-bo and Juren-bo were considered the worst

offenders. On March 11 Anraku-bo was beheaded on the river bank at Rokujo, and Juren-bo was beheaded at Mabuchi. Both died loudly reciting the Nembutsu.

Two sorrowful young nuns were walking up Rokujo Street. Seeing a large crowd of people on the river bank, they went down with beating hearts, and peered stealthily from behind other people.

" Heavens ! " exclaimed the younger nun, who nearly collapsed. The older nun, stouter-hearted, barely was able to support her companion.

They saw the fate of Anraku-bo. The two nuns clasped hands in tears. Then they hurried in the direction of the temple at Shishigadani, hand in hand.

The temple was deserted, without master or worshippers, and not a sound of the Nembutsu could be heard. In front of the temple grounds thick with spring grasses, the ever-punctual cherry blossoms were scattering their petals in the wind.

" Myotei-dono, what shall we do ? "

" Myochi-dono, just because we forced our teachers to perform the ordination rites, they have . . ."

The two nuns embraced each other.

" Because of us, both our teachers died pitiful deaths. What a terrible crime we have committed ! We can only ask for Amida's deliverance. Namu-Amida-Butsu, Namu-Amida-Butsu."

Myochi-ni stood bravely and said, " It's no use crying over what is past. Everything has been destined. Myotei-dono, by way of an apology to our teachers and as an atonement for our sins in creating such tragedies

Chapter 15

THE SWALLOW AND THE WILD
GOOSE

The leading followers of Honen Shonin had to go into exile separately. Honen Shonin and Shakku, who were closely bound by spritual ties as teacher and disciple, were to be exiled, one to Sanuki in the south, and one to Echigo in the north, like the swallow and the wild goose. They could do nothing but sadly bear the lifelong parting.

Honen Shonin, bearing the secular name of Fujii Motohiko, was to leave Kyoto, where he had lived so long, for his place of exile on March 16. He was at the declining age of seventy-five.

On the evening of the 14th, two days before the Shonin's departure, Shakku-bo slipped out of his abode at Okazaki to visit Honen Shonin's quarters at Komatsudani. He was in confinement, but secretly went to bid Honen Shonin a last farewell, for he would not be allowed to see his teacher's departure.

When Shakku knocked on the door, Zenne-bo alone had been attending the teacher, who was reciting the Nembutsu as usual.

Zenne-bo was saying to his teacher, " Will you please recite in a lower voice? Zenshaku-bo and Shogan-bo have just been put to death for reciting the Nembutsu loudly."

" No, I cannot stop the Nembutsu. Even if my tongue be cut in pieces, I cannot refrain from reciting the Buddha's name," Honen Shonin had firmly answered.

Zenne-bo had no reply. He only feared for his teacher.

Seeing that Shakku had come to say good-bye, the Shonin was very happy. The two knew that this was their last meeting. Shakku could not utter a word. Drops of tears fell on the mat.

" I will deliver the masses of people in the south," said the Shonin, " and you can spread the teaching among the people in northern Echigo."

" You have delivered me from the enslavement of birth-and-death ; you have taught me day and night for six years. I shall never forget what I owe you. Unexpectedly I must bid you a sad farewell. I hope you will take special care of yourself due to your advanced age."

" Shakku-bo," said the Shonin, " we who believe in Amida's Vow are fortunate at such time as this, aren't we? This is only a temporary parting. Let us meet again after becoming Buddhas."

After a while, the Shonin's recitation of the Buddha's name was heard again. It was heart-rending to depart, but Shakku had no time to lose.

The good teacher and the disciple, a rare combination

of two great men, parted in this way, with hardly any time to say farewell. Shakku hurriedly left the Shonin's abode at Komatsudani, where the cherry trees looked lonely with the blossoms all fallen.

Chapter 16

THE EXILES

On March 16 in the second year of Shogen, Honen
Shonin, under the secular name Fujii Motohiko, departed from the capital for his place of exile.

His followers in Kyoto lamented to hear that Honen
Shonin, whom they had admired as a living Buddha,
was leaving the capital. He was to depart at ten in the
morning. By then, devout believers, both priests and
laymen, stood in line, like a fence, in front of the gate
at Komatsudani. Twelve people, including Joa-bo,
held the shafts of the palanquin. Crowds of weeping
people, young and old, men and women, accompanied
the Shonin as far as Toba.

On the same day, at six in the morning, Shakku,
given the name Fujii Yoshizane[1], left for his place of
exile, Echigo.

He was Zenshin-bo[1] from now on, for he could not
use the name Shakku any longer. For him there was

[1] The Chinese character for " Yoshizane," the name given to Shakku,
the exile, can be read " Zenshin," and so he was called Zenshin-bo
by his followers.

another heart-breaking separation. It was his parting from his wife Tamahi.

Lady Tamahi had married Zenshin-bo, in obedience to her father Lord Kanezane's order. Ever since, she had been devoted to her husband.

From childhood, she had been impressed deeply by her father's great devotion to Honen Shonin. Whenever there was a sermon given by the Shonin at Tsukinowa's residence, she sat in the audience and listened. Through her father's inspiration, and by her own nature, she had grown up to be religious-minded. Whenever she saw a picture of sages in the beautiful tower in the Pure Land where trailed purple clouds, she was moved deeply.

Being brought up in a good family, she had felt little interest in the opposite sex. But as she arrived at marriageable age, she would sometimes hear her maids talk about her future.

" Our Princess is so beautiful, she can marry any young man of noble birth," someone would say.

" Of course. Hasn't this family produced the former Kanpaku, the advisor to the Emperor? Her marriage would be ill-matched if she were not married to someone of high standing, such as a prince."

" Indeed, her husband would be the luckiest person in all the land for she has such beauty and good disposition."

An older maid lowered her voice and said, " Don't you know that a young son of a certain Chief Councilor of State has his heart set on her? "

" Well, that is welcome news to us."

The maids' eyes brightened with curiosity.

" Ever since he saw the princess at the flower-viewing excursion at Omuro, he could think of no one else.   He could not forget her when he viewed the moon in autumn and the snow in winter.   Finally he disclosed his feelings to his nurse and sent a love-letter to the princess. . . ."

" Really? "

" Yes, it's true.   And it was I who forwarded the letter to her.   But this is a secret.   The nurse was so anxious to have the letter forwarded that I was compelled . . ."

"And what did the princess do? "

" She didn't even touch it.   She returned the letter unopened to the sender.   And I received a severe scolding."

"Ho-ho-ho-ho.   You failed in a romantic errand, didn't you? "

" I have had enough.   I think our princess is a man-hater."

" But recently the princess has been acting quite distracted."

" How   strange ! "   The maids   tilted   their   heads wonderingly.

" How ignorant you all are !   I am the only one that knows.   The man of her heart is a priest ! "

" What, a priest? "

" Yes, that handsome priest who always comes to the villa, attending Honen Shonin."

" How did you know? "

" The princess was restless all the while the priest was alone waiting during the Shonin's sermon, and after the priest left, she seemed quite forlorn."

" How odd ! "

" Being discreet, she keeps her secret in her heart, but she cannot help betraying her feelings. Once I saw her peeping at the priest in the waiting room. When I opened the sliding door, the princess blushed. . . ."

"And does the father know about it ? "

" He loves her very much and considers her only a child, and so he will never suspect," said an elderly waiting-woman thoughtfully.

" Then we must let the Lord know about his somehow."

When her father Kanezane informed her about her coming marriage to Zenshin-bo, the princess was joyous beyond words. She had given up hope, for loving a priest was no better than pursuing a hopeless love. So when she heard this happy news from her father— though she did not know whether he knew her secret— she shed tears of gratitude.

The happy day finally came. Then passed days and months, dreamlike, filled with love, and purified by faith.

But it is the way of the world that happiness is short and sorrow is long. Fate is bound to be envious of a person's good fortune.

The proverb, " The moon is often hid by a cloud, and flowers are often scattered by the storm," governs the ever-changing life of man. Nobody can overcome this.

Cracking thunderbolts roared everywhere. People

were suddenly overtaken by persecution. The Yoshimizu followers of Honen Shonin broke up ; some were
beheaded, and some were exiled. Nothing but tragedy
threatened Lord Tsukinowa.

It was Lady Tamahi's greatest desire to go to Echigo
with her husband, but of course, a convict was not
permitted to take his wife with him.

Kokubu in Echigo was a long way off, and she could
not tell when her husband would be permitted to return
to the capital. The parting, therefore, was heart-
rending. But it could not be helped. Moreover, Zenshin had come near to losing his life. Her father Kanezane, being Zenshin's father-in-law, could not plead
openly for Zenshin's life. So he had asked the Middle
Councilor Rokkaku for help, and finally managed to
have the penalty reduced to that of exile to Echigo.
But since the charge concerned the priest's marriage, it
was out of the question for Zenshin to take Tamahi with
him to Echigo.

The two were destined to part. Their conjugal
life had always had the Buddhist Law for its back-
ground. No matter what they discussed, they had
never forgotten the Buddhist Law. If they had forgotten
it and indulged only in pleasure, the two might just as
well have been condemned to hell. But that was not
the intention of the Shonin, nor of Lord Kanezane,
nor much less of Zenshin, who had unquestioningly
submitted to the insults of the public in the cause of
Buddhism. Lady Tamahi, too, would not have loved
Zenshin, if he had been a sinner.

No matter what religious persecution might be suffered, they would have faith in the Buddha, in accordance with their past Karma—herein lay the source of their conjugal affection.

Lady Tamahi had Zenshin wear a yellowish-brown layman's robe and a soft cap.

"This very day I have realized how precious the Buddha's Law is, the Law that cannot be changed even if one becomes a layman or a priest," she said, holding back her tears.

"The worldly powers believe that they have put me to shame by reducing me to the status of a layman, but this cannot change my faith, you know," he said.

"Even punishment cannot damage the Law," said Tamahi with dignity. But in the next moment, she could not conceal her sorrow. She said, "It will need greater effort for love not to impair the Law."

"Well . . ." said Zenshin-bo with a sorrowful look. "I care nothing about the remoteness of Echigo, but will worry about you. I hope you will take good care of yourself day and night."

"You too must be very careful because of the severe climate. As for myself, please do not worry; Father Kanezane will be with me."

"Rely on Father and wait for my return. Time will fly." Then as if shaking off the pressing sorrow, he said, "Whenever you are anxious to see me, recite 'Namu-Amida-Butsu,' and I will always be with you in your prayer."

"I shall be waiting for you, absorbed in the Nembutsu,

day and night."

"The day before yesterday, when I went to Komatsudani to bid the Shonin farewell," said Zenshinbo, full of deep emotion, "he said that he would deliver the people in the south, and told me to deliver those in the north. He did not look a bit weary, in pite of his age, but on the contrary, looked cheerful and eager to spread Buddhism. I am still young. It would never do if I should fall behind him. In Echigo I am going to deliver the suffering people who are still ignorant of the Amida's merciful desire to save mankind. This would be the best repayment I could make for my indebtedness to the Buddha."

"I am delighted to hear of your noble determination. Meanwhile I shall remain in the capital, and together with Father, shall make efforts to keep up the Nembutsu, even if loud recitation is not permitted, so that the tradition may not die out, at least among the layman believers."

"That is an excellent idea. We would be accumulating virtuous deeds, if we could sacrifice our love for five or ten years and I could deliver those people in northern Echigo."

"Indeed, how wonderful is the Buddha's means of salvation! If it were not for this calamity, we would have been intoxicated by the prosperity of the Nembutsu School, and might have thought only of conjugal happiness. You would be doing an excellent service for generations to come, if you could spread the Buddhist teachings in the remote and deserted regions."

Being well-disciplined under Lord Kanezane, who was a devout believer, Tamahi thus tried to encourage her husband at this sorrowful moment of parting, holding back her sorrow.

Time passed quickly. At the gate there was already a palanquin, ready to carry the exile, Fujii Zenshin.

Chapter 17

THE WAY TO ECHIGO

The palanquin of Fujii Zenshin, the exile, with four
carriers and an officer escort, left the house at Okazaki
and started for the place of exile. Wearing leggings
and footgear, Saibutsu-bo with an iron stick in hand and
Shoshin-bo with a book-case on his back accompanied
the palanquin.

The carriers quickened their pace. By the time they
crossed over the Hinooka Pass, Kyoto had been hidden
behind the mountains, and a rural mood prevailed—
the slow-moving cows, the cherry trees and houses on
the roadside.

Some time later they passed the barrier of Ousaka.
Travelers were usually filled with loneliness after crossing
this barrier. Zenshin, too, was keenly aware that he
had parted from one whom he might never see again.
He recalled the *tanka* by a Manyo poet:

> "The leaves of the bamboo grass
> Rustle on the hillside ;
> But I only think of my love,
> Whom I have left behind."

Zenshin-bo thought of his teacher: "Honen Shonin must have left the capital by this time. I wonder if he has already boarded the river boat at Toba."

When they reached the beach of Uchide at Otsu, Zenshin transferred from the palanquin to a waiting boat.

Asakura Shuzen, whom Lord Tsukinowa had ordered to bid Zenshin farewell, left him here and went back to Kyoto. There was no end to the sorrow of parting.

The boat set forth on the lake of Omi, spreading her sail. How lonely was the journey of an exile at the end of spring! The picturesque view of the lake only increased his sadness.

That night the boat anchored at Chikubu Island, and the party passed the first night of their journey.

The next day they sailed again. Before two in the afternoon, they reached Kaizu and landed. From here the road was a steep mountain path. Zenshin sympathized with the duty of the escorting official. He said: "Thank you for escorting us. From here the path will become rugged. I spent many years on Mount Hiei, walking up and down the rugged paths every day, and so I am a strong walker. But I find that you are from the city. Though it may be the rule to deliver me by palanquin, it is easier for me to walk. This would also cause the carriers less toil. Moreover, I am averse to travel without doing anything, without even preaching to people in such a remote district. So will you please excuse me from riding in the palanquin from today?"

It was natural for the officials and palanquin carriers to become friendly with the exile, travelling together, riding the same boat and stopping at the same inn.

Minamoto Kaneaki, the official in charge, smiled and said, " You are quite right.   To tell the truth, we have been thinking it most troublesome to carry the palanquin along this rugged path.   However, it is required, and difficulties could arise later . . . "

" As for that, please feel at ease.   Of course we don't wear monk's robes, and our heads are not shaved.   We are going to walk, just changing our court headgear to bamboo hats, and our ceremonial robes to plain robes, that's all."

" If that is all you ask, I think it will be all right. Only be careful not to attract the attention of provincial governors and county officials."

" We understand," said Shoshin-bo and Saibutsu-bo.

" Then you may walk starting tomorrow."

Toward the north of Kaizu Station rose the Konami Pass.   From here they would come to the difficult pass called Arichi among the mountains.

While Zenshin-bo was walking in straw sandals, stick in hand, he stumbled over a stone and fell, and hurt his foot.   Shoshin-bo saw the bleeding foot and helped him to stand.

Saibutsu-bo hurriedly wiped the blood and bandaged the foot.

" Can you walk?" he asked.   " We are soon coming to the steep path up Mount Norikura."

" Well, it's nothing," Zenshin-bo replied, and recited a poem:

" Coming to a difficult path
In the mountains
On my way to Echigo,
My foot is stained
With blood ! "

The next day when they reached Yamamoto in Echizen, a crowd of people, who had somehow heard of their coming, were standing on the roadside to welcome them. For the first time Zenshin-bo preached on the ' Other Power' of Amida to these natives of the Hokuriku district.

Next they passed the provinces of Ashiba and Sakai, and entered Kaga. By this time, more and more people had heard of Zenshin-bo and his party. Some of them welcomed the party on the road, and prepared their lodgings, and asked to be instructed about spiritual enlightenment.

From a place called Onoura, they had to cross the sea. Fortunately, the wind was fair, and they were able to land safely on the shore of Kota.

From here Zenshin-bo formally rode in the palanquin, with Asakura, the Lord of Iga, leading the way. Shoshin-bo and Saibutsu-bo walked on either side, and Minamoto Kaneaki followed on horseback. Thus under strict guard, the party finally reached the place of exile, Kokubu in Kubiki County, on March 28, twelve days after leaving Kyoto. Then they immediately entered the residence of Hagihara Toshikage, headman of the county.

Chapter 18

THE COUNTRYMAN'S TEARS

The exile, Fujii Zenshin, was handed over to the county chief, Hagihara Toshikage, by the official in charge.

Toshikage kept Zenshin confined in a room, treating him as an exile. The official came from humble beginnings in the district and had acquired power.

The house for the exile was built at a place called Takeoka. It was a hut, only twelve feet square, with a kitchen and a toilet attached.

Toshikage haughtily commanded Zenshin and the two priests as follows:

" I, Toshikage, have been ordered to keep watch over Fujii Zenshin and two others in attendance. There are certain rules which an exile is expected to obey. Be careful never to disobey any of these rules while you are here."

Quick-tempered Saibutsu-bo glared at Toshikage, feeling the official's attitude was too dictatorial.

But Zenshin calmed him and said that they had to be obedient and persevering.

" We have to instruct this county chief first of all.

If we cannot do this, it is doubtful that we can ever spread Buddhism in this northern district."

Zenshin began to spend his days absorbed in the Nembutsu. He recited it tens of thousands of times, sitting upright without seeing or hearing anything. When he became tired, he would read the Sutras and clarify his thoughts.

He did not resist in any way, nor complain about the chief's treatment. He gladly ate whatever food was given him.

Only rarely when persuaded by Shoshin-bo and others, would he go out, with the chief's permission, to the beach of Kota, and look far out into the broad expanse of the sea and admire the eternity of the universe.

As a result of Zenshin-bo's gentle and calm behavior, Toshikage's attitude gradually changed. He was from the beginning a rustic, without learning or knowledge about Sutras. He was rudely simple, but was not black-hearted.

About a half year after Zenshin-bo and his party arrived, Toshikage's wife, who had been suffering from a chronic disease, grew very ill. She gradually lost weight and it seemed that she would not last very long.

" My wife may not recover this time," he thought. One night he listened to her pitifully weak sighs for a long time.

" She may die. Where is she going when she dies?" he wondered. He had never before thought of such a thing; his only concerns were the land taxes of the region, or hunting.

" I can't imagine her disappearing as if a lamp were blown out.   I wonder where she will go.   Can I ever see her again somewhere?"

He was thinking thus as he walked and suddenly realized he had come to the temple ground of Kokubun-ji.   He saw a faint light in the exile's hut and heard Zenshin reciting the Nembutsu.

" Namu-Amida-Butsu, Namu-Amida-Butsu."   The recitation continued.

Toshikage compared his wife's sighing and moaning with Zenshin-bo's seemingly endless " Namu-Amida-Butsu " and grew very thoughtful.

" I wonder what this ' rebirth into the Pure Land ' is," he mused.   " Does it mean going to a very comfortable place?"

But he immediately decided, " It can't be anything so simple, I'm sure."   He thought that if he asked such a question, his ignorance would be brought to light and ridiculed.

" But it's too late now.   My wife would not have time to seek salvation."

" Would she go to hell?" he thought.   But he soon rejected the thought.   " There can't be such a place."

But he kept wondering.   Whenever he went hunting, he would think, " This wild boar I have just killed did not know anything before it was born.   Even I did not know whether I was to be born a wild boar, or a human being, or a frog, or a snake."

His total ignorance about rebirth made him feel uneasy.

The following day Toshikage came to Zenshin-bo's place. The latter had finished the morning services and was sitting and chanting the Nembutsu. Shoshin-bo and Saibutsu-bo were out.

" I see you are absorbed in the Nembutsu recitation. You have a lot of patience, haven't you?"

" Well, to me, this is the greatest pleasure," Zenshin-bo answered.

Toshikage, who had been studying Zenshin-bo, said, " Why don't you shave the front part of your head? You must feel uncomfortable."

Zenshin's long hair was tied with a piece of creased paper. His unshaven face was heavily bearded.

" No, I am an exile now. Being forbidden to do religious work, I am practically a layman."

" But since the Province Chief in charge says it's all right, you don't have to mind."

" No, no. I have made a vow not to shave until I have received a pardon from the Throne. So though I appreciate your kindness, I would rather remain unshaven."

Toshikage was moved.

" Shaggy hair does not matter at all. But how is your wife?"

" Well, she is getting worse and I think she will not recover this time."

" I'm very sorry to hear it. Namu-Amida-Butsu, Namu-Amida-Butsu."

"What does it mean to be reborn into the Pure Land?" Toshikage ventured to ask. " As you see, I am only a country samurai and do not know anything. . . ."

" It means that one is to be born in a very comfortable place after he has breathed his last here."

" And what discipline must one undergo for it?"

" No discipline is needed. You only have to recite Amida's Name."

" I have heard about the recitation of Amida's Name myself. But how can we understand enlightenment?"

" Enlightenment is not necessary. Only recite Amida's Name, that's all."

" And what kind of place is the Pure Land?"

" As I have said, it is a very pleasant land."

" I heard that you were a famous priest in the capital. But if that is all you can tell me, I feel that you are making fun of me, thinking it's useless to preach to an ignorant person."

" Not at all. There is nothing beyond this in the faith of the Nembutsu School. Even my teacher, the great Honen Shonin, says the same things. He even says that if we knew something more profound than this, the Buddha would not take pity on us."

" Then do you say that persons like me, who have no learning and cannot read the Sutras, can be reborn into the Pure Land?"

" Exactly. They are the very persons to whom the teaching of the Nembutsu is open."

" Then, why should you read the sacred books all the time?"

" Well, because it is my calling. For example, if you want to go across the sea to Onoura, you only have to get on a boat, which will take you to your destination even if you do not know anything. But if you were a boatman, you would have to know the location of capes and big rocks, and the distance. The boat is moved by the wind, and the passengers only have to get on the boat, that's all.

" This is all due to Amida's Vow," he continued. " We only have to get on the ' boat of universal salvation. ' We do not attain rebirth into the Pure Land through our own efforts.

" But if you want to know more about the Land of Bliss, it would be pleasant to read the Sutras. To the priests, it is convenient to know the Sutras in detail. But all shall be reborn into the Pure Land, regardless of whether they know the Sutras. They all go to the same destination, whether they know the Sutras or not."

Zenshin-bo taught Toshikage with sincerity and sympathy.

Toshikage's morale improved. Having learned the Great Path of Easy Practice, he felt great joy.

" I didn't know. I didn't know," he said. " Though living here for a half year, I had no idea that Buddhism was like this. I'm ashamed of my stupidity. Thank you for teaching me such a wonderful thing. People in this district don't know it yet. It is like hiding gold in the mud."

" Now that you know how good it is, hurry and tell your wife about it."

" Really, you are so right. "

Toshikage went home delighted.

Several days later, he came to beg Zenshin to preach a sermon to his wife.

Zenshin preached to her in detail the way to acquire rebirth in the Pure Land, using words she might easily understand.

To a person who had given up all hope of recovery, how wonderful and encouraging was the teaching that said that if one should recite Amida's Name with a whole heart, even once, he would be delivered!

Even a dying person could recite Amida's Name, which is easy to recite and remember.

The hardest thing a person had to bear, even if he had given up everything else, was the separation from the one he loved. The belief that they would be able to see each other again in the Pure Land—such comfort to one's soul!

It was not surprising that Toshikage's dying wife was overjoyed to hear the sermon.

After two months she died, reciting the Nembutsu. Zenshin-bo attended the funeral with his two followers.

Zenshin's great virtue and influence now began to be revealed to the people of the district, for the powerful county chief had begun to respect him as a great teacher.

Chapter 19

TIDINGS FROM THE SWALLOW

The house of exile at Takeoka being too small, Toshikage built a cottage at a place called Hiraoka, and persuaded Zenshin and the others to occupy it.

" Though small, it has more room, and the timber is new. I think it will be more comfortable," said Toshikage.

They moved into this cottage in April, in the second year of Shogen (1208). Though it was a cottage, officially it was the place of confinement for the exile. Zenshin-bo, unshaven as usual and dressed in a plain robe, read Sutras.

Days and months passed: the Echigo districts buried under snow; the early summer rain following the thaw; the clear moon lighting the autumn skies; the chill from the middle of autumn; the sound of the wild geese heard at night.

Once they went to the beach and picked shells, and another time they went to the mountains and gathered ferns.

One day Saibutsu-bo came home with a man who

looked like a merchant.

"Shoshin-bo, Shoshin-bo," he called. "A swallow has just come back. We have tidings from the swallow."

Shoshin-bo anxiously asked, "The swallow's tidings? Is there some encouraging news?"

"This man has brought news from the capital."

The visitor bowed respectfully and said, "Are you Zenshin-bo? I am a medicine salesman of Echigo, visiting the capital once every summer. While in the capital I heard of the Nembutsu School, and went to Yoshimizu to hear a sermon. Then I was converted to the Nembutsu School.

"But when I heard that the recitation of the Nembutsu was prohibited, and that the high priests at Yoshimizu were in trouble, I was panic-stricken. Then taking a boat trip to Sanuki on business, I called on Honen Shonin at Komatsu-no-sho."

Zenshin-bo leaned forward anxiously asking, "And how was the Shonin?"

"I found that he was very well. The magistrate's treatment is considerate, the place being Lord Tsukino-wa's land. The Shonin had been enjoying the Nem-butsu."

"That makes me feel at ease."

"I said to the Shonin, 'I come from Echigo. When I go back I intend to call on Zenshin-bo, so shall I take a message to him?'"

"Hmm, what did he say?"

"He said, 'Tell him that we are living a peaceful life; that the most important thing is the deliverance

of the people in the northern districts; and though
separated from each other, north and south, we are
always meeting in the recitation of the Nambutsu.'
This was his message."

" What a gratifying message it is!"

" The tidings from the capital make me feel relieved.
Make yourself comfortable," said Shoshin-bo cheerfully,
thanking the salesman for his trouble.

Then they talked about the news from the capital
and religious subjects.

Everybody felt nostalgic about their home, especially
Saibutsu-bo and Shoshin-bo, who were not exiles.

More lonely days and months went by.

The winter season veiled the countryside in gloomy
gray. Snow fell thick and fast in this northern land
every day, and the village of Kokubu was often buried
under ten or twenty feet of snow. Sometimes travelers
could not pass.

During the summer, grass would be cut and dried; in
the autumn trees would be cut and rice ground into
powder—thus the people would make preparations for
the winter confinement. They could not help living
like insects and snakes until the snow would begin to
melt. During the winter, the farmers had no work
to do. Having no other employment they suffered from
poverty.

Zenshin-bo could not help pitying the people. It
would give them comfort, if he could preach the
teaching of the Nembutsu.

He realized he had to spread the Nembutsu. For this

purpose he had to live among the people for a long time, the thought.

A new year came round, and once the snow ceased for several days, which was quite unusual. The sun shone for the first time in many days. Mountains and fields were masses of white snow, and only the hungry birds could be heard.

One day Shoshin-bo was standing at the door of the cottage, gazing at the snow, when he saw a man come tumbling over the snow toward him in snow shoes and a long stick in his hand.

" Is this where Zenshin-bo stays? I come with a message from Lord Tsukinowa in the capital," he said.

Shoshin-bo was surprised. " Well, well, thank you for going through so much trouble," he said. " Please come in."

Shoshin-bo led the man in and called, " Saibutsu-bo, Saibutsu-bo, there are tidings again from the swallow."

Saibutsu-bo came out rejoicing. " Thank you for bringing the message from Lord Tsukinowa."

But the messenger's head drooped. He looked dejected.

Zenshin-bo stopped his chanting and joined the group.

" Is this Zenshin-bo? I have brought a letter from Lady Tamahi."

Zenshin-bo hastened to open the letter, which said:

" I always gaze at the northern sky, thinking of you leading a life of confinement in Echigo, buried in snow.

" But I remember what you said when you left the capital—that this was an expedient means of the Buddha to spread Buddhism among the northern people. And so I cheer myself and recite the Nembutsu.

" My father Kanezane had been troubled and low-spirited since the Nembutsu prohibition. But recently Honen Shonin's exile has been discussed at the Court, and thanks to Father's efforts, it seems possible that the Shonin would be shifted to Kawachi, not far from the capital, though not yet permitted to return. Father was very happy to hear this. I do not know whether it was due to this relief from mental strain, but he became ill and was confined to bed since last December. He gradually got worse, and in spite of good care and medical treatment, he died on January 10.

"As he had been especially affectionate to me from childhood, I was in the deepest of sorrow and was at a loss. I think you can understand.

" Father had been a devout Buddhist. I am certain he attained rebirth of the highest degree in the Land of Bliss, and I feel relieved. If I had lacked faith at such an occasion, I don't know how I could have consoled myself. I realized how precious the Nembutsu is.

" But he had been anxious about you constantly, and had been waiting to see you again. When I think of it, I cannot help feeling sorry for him. But everything is due to our past Karma, and so it can't ever he helped. There is nothing we can do except to recite the Nembutsu.

" I wish you would take very good care of yourself. Be especially careful not to catch cold from the evening chill.

" Honen Shonin's penalty is to be reduced. Yours, too, may be reduced so that you could live nearer the capital. I am looking forward to it.

" When will we ever be able to look at the moon and
the flowers, hand in hand, and talk about our indebtedness to he Buddha? I always recall your instruction at
parting and whenever I miss you, I recite the Nembutsu.
The sorrow of losing my beloved father has affected my
writing, I'm afraid, for which I beg your pardon.

Yours lovingly,

Tamahi "

When Zenshin-bo had read the letter, he put it back
in the envelope and quietly said to Shoshin-bo and
Saibutsu-bo, " Lord Tsukinowa Kanezane passed away
on January 10."

" What, Lord Kanezane? "

The two looked at each other sadly.

" It's the way of the world. We can only chant the
Nembutsu for the happiness of his soul," said Zenshin-
bo.

All held back their tears.

" But Honen Shonin's penalty will be reduced and
he will be moved to Kawachi, not far from the capital,
it is said."

They all sat before the Buddha's altar and held a
service.

The messenger was given warm hospitality. Zenshin-
bo wrote a long, warm letter to Tamahi and gave it to
the messenger. The latter said he wanted to deliver the
answer to Lady Tamahi as quickly as possible, and so
he started back for the capital, braving the snow. The
thick snow covered his footprints.

After that came days covered with snow.

Chapter 20

FORSAKING THE BLOSSOMS

A year passed, and then another year, and finally Zenshin-bo saw the spring of the fifth year of his exile.

Minbu Toshikage, the county chief, was now Zenshin-bo's devout follower. He summoned people of the district and secretly made arrangements for religious sermons. It was true of all devout believers: they were unable to suppress their strong faith, whatever their duties might have been in public.

Rumors from the capital said that the prohibition of the Nembutsu there had become less severe as time went by.

Honen Shonin had already been permitted to return to the Kinai districts, and he was actually living in the temple, Katsuodera, in Settsu Province. Such being the conditions in the capital, even if sermons were delivered to the natives in this far-off northern district, it seemed a mere oversight on the part of the county chief.

In this way, devout believers in the Nembutsu had been gathering around Zenshin-bo.

The heavy snowfalls had at last nearly ended, and the

plum buds were about to open on the branches facing south. The patent-medicine salesman came back again with welcome tidings from the capital.

" On Mount Hiei, it is said that the monkeys supposed to be sacred to the god Hiesanno, ran riot and climbed up the temple buildings and towers, and overturned Sutra cases, so that they were at a loss, having no idea what to do with them. Strange to say, at the same time in Nara, the deer, sacred to the god Kasuga Myojin, ran out of control. This was common talk in the capital.

" And when they begged hastily for a divine message, it became known that the gods were furious because high priests of the Nembutsu School had been punished. So they want the priests to be pardoned. Though I do not know if this is true, I can say for certain that the attitude against the Nembutsu has become very lenient in the capital.

" Moreover, it is said that the ex-Emperor had a strange dream. And Honen Shonin, it is rumored, will be permitted to return to the capital from Katsuo-dera before long. I'm sure you too, will be pardoned before long. Therefore, it is best to bide your time, isn't it? Your sufferings will not be long."

Not only this salesman's tidings, but a letter from Shokaku Hoin, Zenshin-bo's fellow disciple at Yoshi-mizu, also referred to the same news.

With the thawing of the snow, it seemed that Fortune had begun to smile even upon the exile in the northern district.

In the meantime the cherry blossoms bloomed in the garden of the abode at Hiraoka.

" Saibutsu-bo, it seems that brighter days are coming."

" Yes, we shall be able to return to the cpital before long."

" O how I long to see the Kamo Stream!"

"Shoshin-bo, look! The cherry-blossoms have opened so beautifully. Since spring is late here, maybe those at Higashiyama (in Kyoto) are in full bloom, or maybe they have begun to fall."

Zenshin-bo also came out on the veranda and gazed at the blossoms.

" Flowers bloom and fall according to the cosmic law of Karma," he said. " When I took the ordination at the age of nine, the cherry trees in the garden of Shoren-in were in bloom. When I called on Honen Shonin to say good-bye two days before I left the capital, the cherry trees at Komatsudani were also in bloom. Cherry blossoms really make us meditative."

He seemed to be lost in thought.

One day, four or five days later, a messenger suddenly arrived on a post horse.

" I am Otsuki Yukitsura, a retainer serving Lord Tsukinowa," he said, panting. " I have come with an urgent message."

" And what can that be?" Saibutsu-bo and Shoshin-bo asked.

" It's very sad news," he said, weeping. " Lady Ta-mahi, who had been heart-broken since the death of her father, suddenly became ill at the end of last month.

We thought it was a minor illness, but she suddenly grew worse, and passed away on the second of this month."

Zenshin-bo was shocked at the news. He could not conceal his sorrow. Large tears fell on his robe. The others averted their eyes and sobbed sorrowfully.

After a while, Zenshin-bo wiped his tears and said, " I really was mistaken. Though I know very well that man's life is uncertain, I am overcome with sorrow when I actually face it. Tamahi has happily attained rebirth into the Pure Land. Her Karmic ties with this suffering world have come to an end. She must be in the Pure Land now, meeting with Lord Kanezane, surrounded by Bodhisattvas and listening to Amida's sermons. What is there for me to lament?"

Shoshin-bo then added, " It makes me think that those who died have really eased themselves of their burden. They must be greatly relieved. Those who are left behind do not think about their own difficult life, and think that they are more fortunate than the dead. And so they pine for the dead. But how can those remaining be more fortunate?"

Saibutsu-bo agreed, saying, " You are right. During these five years in this northern district, we have had far more suffering than pleasure. Happy days have been few."

The messenger samurai said, " I hear that a holy man does not feel any suffering or happiness."

" The greatest bliss is found where there is no suffering or happiness. It is written in the Sutras that man's sentiment always changes—he rejoices and he grieves. This is the state of us common mortals," said Zenshin-bo.

He called himself a common mortal. He did not try to conceal his sorrow.

They all gathered for a wake service that night, burning incense.

Since he heard of the death of Tamahi, Zenshin-bo felt that his longing for the capital had vanished. The capital seemed empty to him. He felt as though he had suddenly grown old and empty of emotion.

Though he tried to forget, the memories of his bygone days with Tamahi came back to him.

" What brief ties of marriage ours have been!" he thought to himself. " What a pity it was that she should leave for the ' Western Land ' (the Land of Bliss), for my return to the capital had been nearing, and the cherry-blossoms were at their best. She was like the wild goose that went back to its home, leaving the blossoms."

He felt at home in the silence of the northern land. In silence he passed the first month and the second month. Aside from reciting the Nembutsu, he could not be interested in anything.

No matter how hard he tried to cheer himself, sadness immediately overcame him. He no longer resisted his grief and only recited the Nembutsu.

One of Honen Shonin's teachings came home to him for the first time: " It's useless to try to utter the Nembutsu, after having suppressed distracting thoughts. Utter the Nembutsu, leaving distracting thoughts as they are."

The May rain was over and summer came. Even the sight of children chasing fireflies along the rice fields, made him recall the short-lived Tamahi. Indeed, man's life was no better than that of the firefly that died on the grass.

Autumn came, the moon rose in the clear sky and insects began to chirp. His memory of a cricket cage, especially, was heart-breaking. In autumn, Tamahi used to hang one from the eaves. He remembered Tamahi and how they had listened to the crickets' chirping and talked all night through.

" There is nothing that goes straight to one's heart as the singing of the cricket, is there?" she had said, listening to the insect. The way she looked then still remained in his memory.

The autumn advanced, and frost came to the northern district at night. He was more and more filled with loneliness.

At last winter came again.

In December, a public messenger arrived with an Imperial command dated November 17. He also brought with him an official notice from the Cabinet.

Hagihara Minbu Toshikage, in the capacity of county chief, gave Fujii Zenshin the Cabinet notice of his pardon and the Imperial Edict. The notice said:

" Fujii Zenshin, exiled to Kokubu in Echigo province in the spring of the first year of Shogen: the above person had been exiled, due to an appeal made by Mount Hiei, but is now pardoned by an Imperial order."

Zenshin-bo received the papers respectfully. The messenger also reported that on the same day Honen Shonin was also permitted to return to the capital.

Both Shoshin-bo and Saibutsu-bo rejoiced, as if restored to life.

But somehow Zenshin-bo did not feel as happy. Only the thought of meeting Honen Shoin made him wish to return to the capital.

Shoshin-bo and Saibutsu-bo began to make preparations to return.

Zenshin-bo, who had not shaved his head for a long time, had it clean shaven. His bushy beard was also shaved.

Toshikage saw Zenshin-bo in his priest's garb for the first time. In a light blue robe and a five-piece stole, with rosary in hand, he looked distinctive, with dignity and wisdom.

Saibutsu-bo could not sit still. He went to the Kota beach to see when the boat was leaving.

Toshikage regretted their departure and said sadly, " I am very happy that you are permitted to go back. For five years, we have had a good teacher, from whom we received instructions day and night. How encouraging it was to us! If you leave us now, we shall all feel distraught and lonely."

Zenshin-bo felt sorry for them and kindly consoled them, saying, " As I always say, in the Nembutsu teaching, you just recite " Namu-Amida-Butsu.' No learning and no knowledge of the Sutras are necessary. There is no reason to feel abandoned.

" I'm going back to the capital, not because I dislike the provinces and love the gay capital, but because my teacher Honen Shoin has been permitted to return to the capital, and I would like to see him after these many years.

" If you feel lonely because you cannot see me, I will make a drawing of myself and leave it as a momento.

" After meeting the Shonin, I may again make a preaching tour to this district, so please do not be discouraged."

From that day Zenshin-bo faced a mirror every day, drawing a portrait of himself. He was surprised to find that in five years he had grown old, and now appeared to be another person.

Shoshin-bo had put his pannier in order, and had some rope and boards ready so that he could shoulder it at any moment. Saibutsu-bo had three pairs of snow-shoes and hats and sticks ready, and waited for the moment to start.

However, the roads were blocked with snow, and people could not pass. Finally a report came with the coming of the new year: " A traveler came from Shinano today, crossing the Tozama Pass. Therefore, if one takes the route from Shinano to Kiso, he may be able to go to the capital even now. But the Hokuriku Road is impassable at present."

Shoshin-bo and Saibutsu-bo could not wait any longer.

Finally on January 28 the three started, braving the snow. The way to Shinano had less snow than the

Echigo route. But the way to Kiso was so snowbound that men and horses could not pass. They were compelled to go round Kozuke and take the Tokaido Highway to the capital. So they turned back and crossed the Usui Pass and headed for Matsuida. While they were walking, they came across a priest in black robe who looked like a follower of the Nembutsu School.

Passing by, the priest called in surprise, " Aren't you Zenshin-bo ?"

" Why, it's Chimyo-bo. What a surprise to see you at such a place."

" I see you are going back to the capital, due to the recent pardon."

" Certainly. Although my mind is eager to see Honen Shonin, the roads are blocked with snow, and we are compelled to take a roundabout way."

Chimyo-bo suddenly became tearful.

" Then Zenshin-bo, you haven't yet heard the news ?"

" What is the matter ?"

" Honen Shonin returned to the capital on November 20, but soon afterwards became ill, and finally passed away on the 25th of this month."

Zenshin-bo was struck with astonishment. He put his hands over his face and sobbed, his body shaking. He tried hard to bear it, but failed, and fell on the ground and began to weep bitterly.

Saibutsu-bo and Shoshin-bo tried to comfort their teacher and patted his shoulders. But they could do nothing except leave him alone for some time. The two had never seen their teacher weep so bitterly.

Zenshin-bo wept like a child for a long time. But when he stopped weeping and raised his face, his expression had changed completely. There was no longer any trace of yearning. His attitude was that of resignation, of having given up everything.

Shoshin-bo said, " You may well weep, but no matter how much we weep there is no help for it. Now it is best to return to the capital quickly and consider the matter with the Yoshimizu followers of the Shonin, so that the Nembutsu School may be re-established."

When Shoshin-bo thus tried to persuade Zenshin-bo, the latter shook his head and said, " No, no. I have given up the idea of going back to the capital."

" Why is this?" asked Saibutsu-bo in surprise.

" I was in a hurry to go back just because I wanted to meet Honen Shonin again. Now that he is gone, there is nothing in the capital that attracts my interest. It is useless to go back."

" For all that, I fail to see why you should remain in this remote district."

" When I bade farewell to the Shonin at Komatsudani, he told me to deliver the uninformed people in the remote districts, and his voice still lingers in my memory. When I think of it, that voice of his has become his last message to me.

" I am sure that people living near the capital do not lack the opportunity to come in contact with both Buddhism and culture. But those in the northern and eastern districts do not. Their lives are indeed pitiful, as I have seen while living in confinement in Echigo for five years.

" During these five years, I have lost Lord Tsukinowa, Tamahi, and Honen Shonin. I feel as though I were in a wilderness. What is the use of living in the gay city?

" Now it is my wish to travel in the remote districts and preach the Buddha's teachings to the people there. This is now my only desire."

As Zenshin-bo's resolution was unshakable, his followers could no longer say anything.

Zenshin-bo became a true spiritual leader from that day on. He realized his mission. At this occasion he changed his name to Shinran—' Shin ' from Tenjin-bosatsu,[1] and ' ran ' from Donran-daishi.[1]

He arrived at this decision because Lord Kanezane and Tamahi and Honen Shonin had all passed away and the gay, promising world was suddenly shut out. What could this be, except Amida's way to lead him to his spiritual awakening?

---

[1] Two of the seven Patriarchs of the Nembutsu School—Tenjin of India, Donran of China.

Chapter 21

HERE AND THERE IN ECHIGO

Shinran made up his mind to spread the Buddha's teachings. When he decided to devote his whole life to this work among the uninformed people in the remote districts, indifferent to fame and fortune, he felt love welling up within him.

To commemorate this resolution of his, he went to pray for three weeks at the temple Zenkoji, by way of Shinano and crossing Mt. Togakushi.

" O Amida of Zenkoji! Help me realize my aspirations to deliver all people! Even the ignorant and dull-witted, all are my children. If I ever work for name or profit, please take my life away from me!"

He prayed with his whole heart.

His own deliverance had become certain. From now on he would carry out his desire to deliver innumerable people.

When he entered the province of Echigo, passing Shinano, the first things he saw were the three mountains of Myoko, Kurohime, and Iizuna rising before him. The snowy top of Mt. Myoko shone brightly, though it was April.

When he started to climb Koizumo, after leaving Sakamoto, he saw clouds trailing in the clear sky, red with evening glow. The sight was so marvelous, he could not help feeling that beyond the red glow in the western sky lay Amida's land.

At last the party reached their old abode in Kokubu.

Hagihara Toshikage was delighted. He had taken good care of the place for them, without changing a single thing.

" Not knowing if I could ever see you again in this world, I have been gazing at your portrait every day. It is like a dream to see you so soon."

" We were fated to meet," said Shinran. " On our way to the capital we heard of the death of Honen Shonin, and my desire to go back vanished. I decided to spread Buddhist teachings among the people of remote districts, and so I came back."

" How thankful we are!" said Toshikage, beaming with joy. " You have not yearned for the flowery city, but have been true to your word, not forgetting the people in this remote district. You are, indeed, Shonin of great compassion. Please stay here long and preach and instruct us."

" No. Though I appreciate your kindness, it is not wise to stay at one place. Those who wish to recite the Nembutsu are all my brethren, my children. I must travel to every corner of the district, to come in contact with the people. I shall stay here as long as I feel it is best."

Toshikage shed tears and said, " Really, I was thinking selfishly. Being so delighted to see you again, I
have thought only about ourselves, and not about all
the people at large. Please stay and awaken us as long
as you can."

They stayed in Kokubu for two weeks.

Toshikage circulated notices and gathered people,
both young and old, men and women, from all over the
district. Eager to take a look at the Shonin, who had
been an exile in Kokubu, a large crowd gathered.

Toshikage made an introductory speech:

" As you have already heard, the Shonin suffered
confinement for five years in a humble exile's hut in
Hiraoka. He was put in my charge, and at first I treated
him only as an exile. But observing his daily perse-
verance and industry, I realized that he was no ordinary
person. I came to regard him with respect. When
my wife became ill and neared death, the Shonin kindly
preached the Easy Path of Amida's Power, and she died
happily, reciting the Nembutsu.

" In November last year, the Shonin was officially
pardoned and freed from exile. But not wishing to
return to the gay capital, he has begun a preaching tour
all over the country, in order to spread the doctrine of
the Buddha among us.

" Therefore, while he is here I hope you will all listen
to his sermons on our deliverance through Amida's
Power."

He spoke with great feeling and tears. The crowded
audience became perfectly silent.

Shinran Shonin closed his eyes and uttered Amida's Name. He gently smiled and said:

" There are the Buddha's wisdom and man's wisdom. If we say that a learned man is wise and a peasant is ignorant, we are talking about the rank in man's wisdom. But the difference between man's wisdom and the Buddha's wisdom is far greater than the difference between an adult's and an infant's wisdom. No matter how hard a man may try, he only follows the birth-and-death cycle in the Six Evil Realms, like the summer insects that keep on flying round the fire. So the Buddha has provided a way, like a life-boat of Great Love and Compassion. The Buddha says, ' Just ride on it. Avoid useless talk and worry, for that will only cause distractions! ' The mother only pulls the drowning child out of the water—she will not tell him to swim.

" This is what we mean by rebirth into the Pure Land by Amida's Power. Only rely on Amida, call his Name, and the motherly love of Amida will take care of everything for us.

" It is the prejudiced mind of common mortals that says that the peasants are ignorant, the villagers are stupid. It is not said by the Buddha's mind, which is vast and boundless and absolute.

" My twenty years' learning and devotion on Mount Hiei proved to be a burden, hampering my rebirth into the Pure Land, and so were useless to me.

" I only recite ' Namu-Amida-Butsu,' and through the power of Amida's Vow, shall be reborn into the Pure Land.

" That is all. Don't you see how easy it is, all of you? "

" My teacher Honen Shonin was considered the most learned scholar on Mount Hiei, but he recited the Nembutsu along with illiterate, ordinary people. He even said that the Buddha would not particularly favor the wise men of our faith. It would be terrible, you know, if the Buddha should forsake a man saying, ' Then do as you like with your own power.'

" Did you all understand what I said? Anyone who will recite the Nembutsu from this moment will be assured of attaining rebirth into the Pure Land, exactly in the same way as I will be.

" Oh, how overwhelmed with gratitude we should be, for the teaching of the Nembutsu, the Easy Path of Amida's Power! "

Shinran finished his sermon and recited aloud, " Namu-Amida-Butsu."

Then, like an echo, the sound of the Nembutsu arose and spread among the audience.

Two weeks passed. The villagers were all delighted to have received such glorious teachings for the first time. At parting they clung to Shinran's sleeve, but he at last left Kokubu.

Toshikage said to Shinran in tears, " Where are you going next in your preaching tour? Will you please let us know? "

" Like the floating clouds and running water, I go wherever my Karmic destiny takes me. Our abode is under a tree and on the stone like Sakyamuni's. I

know not where I go. Wherever the Nembutsu is recited, wherever distressed people live, there I shall be,
no matter how dreary the shore or how remote the
village may be. If our destinies permit, we shall meet
again. Do not neglect the Nembutsu."

Shinran Shonin left Kokubu and started north along
the Hokuriku Road.

On his right stretched the distant mountains of Shinano and Echigo provinces, and on his left was the vast
expanse of the rough Japan Sea. Shinran and his party
walked along the seashore, wetting their sandals.

Summer clouds lingered at the top of Yoneyama
(mountain). It was a blazing hot day. They walked
along a steep path, wiping off perspiration and dragging
their feet. But toward evening, the wind changed.
Soon clouds spread over the sky, and it began to rain
heavily.

They took shelter under the eaves of houses and at
wayside shrines, where they squeezed water from their
robes. The rain became heavier and showed no signs
of stopping. So, putting oil-paper raincoats over their
shoulders, they walked in the rain, encouraging each
other.

When they reached the banks of the river Terakawa,
muddy water in rushing torrents was carrying away
bridges and huts. The water overflowed the banks and
ran into the rice fields.

" It is impossible to cross the river now. We had
better go back and ask for a night's lodging at some
house," they said.

They stood under the eaves of a house and asked for a night's shelter.

"We are priests on a pilgrimage. We are dripping wet in the heavy rain and need help. Please may we spend the night with you?"

No answer could be heard in the noisy rain.

Saibutsu-bo knocked and called at the door.

The mistress of the house finally opened the door, her sash trailing behind her. She held out a torch. When she saw that the visitors were priests, she said harshly, "We are fishermen. We have nothing to do with priests. Go away!"

"Some corner of a hut or barn, or anywhere will do. As you see, we are drenched with rain. . . ."

"We are mere fishermen. We catch and sell smelly fishes every day and make a living. I think you have the wrong house," she said.

"No. Those things are nothing to us."

"Ho-ho-ho-ho. Then you must be corrupt priests. I refuse all the more!"

"Don't be so hard on us. Couldn't you please give us shelter for the night?"

"You stubborn priests! Here, my good man . . ." She called to her husband. "Three priests are asking shelter for the night. What are we going to do?"

"What? Priests?" asked a drunken man's voice. "Well, refuse them!"

"I said no, but they keep on asking."

"I'm tired out from fishing all day, and want to enjoy my drink before going to bed. And now this . . ."

" You hear him? " she said to the priests.   " It's no use, so go away."

" Never mind us, then, but won't you let in just the Shonin? "

" What?   The Shonin? "   The husband came to the door.   His breath smelled of cheap *sake*.[1]

"A Shonin to stay in a fish-stinking house?   Or are you going to drink sake with me and talk about women? "

" There is nothing that can offend us, for all men, no matter what sort, are our fellows."

" How corrupt you are!   No, we can't have you! "

" May I ask you once more? " said Shoshin-bo, controlling his anger.   " Won't you let Shonin stay for the night, please? "

" Let us alone.   Beggar priests, don't disturb our night-cap.   Wife, come on, let's have a drink and go to bed."

Shinran and the others were utterly helpless.   They pushed close to the door, but the rain soaked them to the skin.

The three stood close together.   People are less troubled when they are close together.   When they had resigned themselves to their troubles, all three spontaneously began to chant the Nembutsu.   While they were doing this in unison, they entered a state of *samadhi*[2], free from all ideas and thought.   They were unaware of the rain that drenched them.

Unaware of the passing of the night, they went on

[1] Japanese rice wine

[2] Absorption

reciting the Nembutsu with their whole hearts, forgetting themselves.

There was no heaven, no earth, no rain, no house; only the Six-Character Myogo (Amida's Name).

The couple, who had been fast asleep after their drinking, suddenly awoke and heard the clear sound of the Nembutsu.

The husband felt thirsty and went to the kitchen for some water. He had completely recovered from the effects of the wine.

He still heard the Nembutsu. Recalling the visitors, he opened the door a little and peeped out. The three priests, standing together, were reciting the Nembutsu in a state of absorption.

There was no desire, no fear, nor anger on their faces. They seemed to have forgotten about this house. They did not notice him either.

Then, were they asleep? No. They were wide awake, with clear eyes.

The man had never seen such a sight. He was overcome by strange feelings. He quietly called his wife and took her to the door. Rubbing her sleepy eyes, the wife saw the priests. The two were overwhelmed with fear.

Due to the great power of the *samadhi*, a living Buddha had come and practically illuminated the spot.

The couple changed their clothes, and rushed to the door with a light. They prostrated themselves before Shinran and his followers.

" I sincerely apologize to you for my rudeness last

evening, even though I was drunk. Please come into the house."

They welcomed the three into the house. The wife started a fire and dried the wet clothes.

"Wonderful priests, may I ask who you are?"

"This is Shinran Shonin, a great teacher of the Nembutsu School of the 'Other Power,'" said Saibutsu-bo.

"Saibutsu-bo," Shinran interrupted, "don't exaggerate. We are wandering monks, spreading the doctrine of the Nembutsu teaching of Amida's Easy Path. These northern provinces seem to call us spiritually, and so we began our preaching tour, starting from Kokubu."

"What kind of teaching is this Nembutsu of the Easy Path of the 'Other Power'?"

"It is a teaching in which we attain rebirth into the Pure Land, not through our own efforts, but through the power of Amida's Vow, by reciting Amida's Name."

"I saw you reciting the Nembutsu with all your heart, which deeply impressed me."

"We were only reciting the Nembutsu, not knowing anything."

"I believe you must be noble teachers, but I do not understand your saying that smelling fish and *sake* would not trouble you."

"Well, in our Nembutsu teaching, anyone can be reborn into the Pure Land by reciting the Nembutsu. If he is a fisherman, he recites the Nembutsu as a fisherman, and if he is a merchant, he recites it as a merchant. We do not attain rebirth into the Pure Land by ' self-power ' or accumulating merit."

" Can a rascal like me be reborn into the Pure Land, then? "

" Of course.   The most wicked person, too, can be reborn into the Pure Land, if he recites the Nembutsu. In the first place, the Nembutsu is for the delivery of such people."

The wife also asked, " Can a rude woman like me be delivered, too? "

" Yes, you can.   Don't look at yourself and worry; only rely on the power of the Buddha's Vow.   It is like relying on your husbands' skill when you sail far out to sea with him."

The husband was greatly moved.   " I am an illiterate, ignorant fisherman, and my wife is a worthless woman. But there is a Buddha who delivers us in spite of our faults.   He says, ' Come with empty hands—no present is necessary.'   This is strange, but it is possible, isn't it?"

" That's it.   Any person is capable of being good and honest.   It is because the Buddha has put His seed into that person's heart.   This is what we call the Buddha-nature in all men.   No matter how compassionate the Buddha is, it is useless if a man does not respond.   But even the most wicked people have the seed."

" Thank you for giving us such happy tidings.   I feel as though I have been awakened from sleep.   I feel inspired."

" The day is dawning."

" It seems the rain has stopped."

" Won't you have some boiled rice with hot water? We don't have much to give you in our humble home."

The wife happily began to prepare breakfast.

The husband brought some writing paper and said, " Won't you please write Amida's Name on this, so that we can hang it on the wall and recite it day and night? We will be content with the Six-Character Myogo. Even if we wished to learn something more, it might be beyond our power of understanding." Then he laughed loudly.

" That's it. That's the best way," said Saibutsu-bo, laughing. " I am not good at learning myself."

Then he suddenly asked, " You said your name is Kakizaki, didn't you?"

" Yes, that's right."

Saibutsu-bo, picking up a fan at his side, composed a comic poem:

> " We asked Kakizaki (Persimmon Cape)
> Hesitatingly
> For a night's lodging,
> When the master's heart (the sour persimmon)
> Became a mellowed persimmon."

The fisherman laughed loudly, scratching his head. " You're right. I'm a mellowed persimmon. A green, bitter persimmon became mellow overnight."

" It is what we call faith that gives us common mortals a ' straight-entrance ' into the Pure Land," said Shoshin-bo seriously.

They all forgot about the quarrel of the night before; they all opened their hearts and became one in the Nembutsu.

Chapter 22

THE MIRACLE OF THE PURPLE BAMBOO

The Shinano River, flowing quietly through the broad rice-fields, reflected the autumn sunlight. Shinran made his temporary home in a village called Toyano on the east bank of the river. Kanbara County was large, containing many villages, and Toyano was the most deserted of all the villages.

The villagers' dialect, too, was different from that of northern Echigo. It seemed coarse in comparison.

It was harvest time, but the rice plants had suffered greatly from blight that year, and so the crop was only half the usual amount. The peasants stood on the ridges between the fields, not knowing what to do.

Somehow Shinran did not feel like leaving the village. He built a cottage just large enough for them to sit in, and wondered how to spread the teaching of the ' Other Power ' among the villagers.

Strange to say, the people did not care to listen to the teaching.

Shinran walked among them, preaching, in spite

of rain or wind, but the only reactions were scorn and abuse. It was only on rare occasions that he was able to edify anyone.

Even the gentle Shoshin-bo heaved a sigh and recited:

> " Isn't there anyone
> In this village,
> Who has lost a parent?
> Alas, no one bends
> Before the wind of the Law ! "

" What stubborn people they are! " said the quick-tempered Saibutsu-bo. " There are others everywhere waiting to be edified. I don't see why we have to stay here so long." He felt depressed.

But Shinran did not forsake the stubborn, irreligious people. He kindly preached the teaching as always. But not a soul was drawn to him.

That year came to an end, covered with snow, and a new year began. Still, there were no believers.

" This must be the Buddha's way of leading one to spiritual awakening," said Shinran. " We should never be too optimistic, thinking everyone will eagerly follow if we merely preach the Buddha's teachings."

One day for no apparent reason, Shinran stuck a purple bamboo stick, which he had received, into the back yard of his cottage. Then he closed his eyes and prayed:

" Sakyamuni Buddha, and Amida, please witness which is more difficult: for this bamboo branch to take root in the ground, or for me to plant one follower of the Nembutsu in this locality! "

Shoshin-bo and Saibutsu-bo looked at each other, thinking their teacher's mind might be disturbed.

Shinran went on preaching patiently and untiringly, day and night.

If he could not get a single follower in this village, the teaching of the Easy Practice of the ' Other Power ' would not have power to deliver the poor people, he thought.

It was early summer and the rainy season was nearing. One cloudy day, as Shinran sat at his desk reading the scriptures, a visitor arrived.

" I am Shinjuro of Hirashima, a farmer of this village," he said. " I have been on Sado Island, working in a gold mine. I came to see the master here."

" I am the master," said Shinran.

" The villagers told me that you are preaching a faith called the Easy Path of the ' Other Power.' May I ask what kind of teaching it is? "

" It is a teaching by which we can be born into the Pure Land solely by the Buddha's Vow to deliver us, not by our deeds."

Shinjuro slapped his knee and said, " I see. I thought there might be such a teaching and I was right."

" It is the Nembutsu teaching, through which common mortals are able to go straight to the Pure Land. It was taught by Sakyamuni of India, Zendo of China, and Honen Shonin of our country."

" Please let me tell you about myself. I was a failure in this village and went to work in a gold mine on Sado

Island. I later became a foreman in charge of many miners. One day poisonous fumes filled one of the levels and there was immediate danger of a landslide. Somehow I did not think about myself; I only thought of saving the lives of all the miners. I rushed into the level and ran about shouting, 'Look out! Get out quickly!' I thought I heard their cries, but I fainted, being overcome by the fumes.

"When I regained consciousness, I had been given medical treatment in a hut. This is the scar from my injury.

"I then thought to myself that though people said the gold mine was a hell, human beings live in a kind of hell. I wondered then whether there was a Buddha of great love and mercy who could save every one of us, by shouldering all our sins.

"I came back to my home village after a long absence, and decided to buy some rice-fields and stay. Then I happened to hear about the teaching of the Easy Path of the 'Other Power.' This reminded me of my past experience and so I came to see you."

Shinran was very happy. "Shinjuro," he said, "that's most praiseworthy. You have penetrated into the very heart of Amida's Vow. Now it's not necessary to speak lengthily to you. What you developed in your own mind is the real teaching, positively based on the Sutras. So you have reason to rejoice."

"That makes me feel wonderful. Life has become bright and hopeful to me."

Saibutsu-bo, deeply moved, said, "In contrast to

Shinjuro's intelligence, how dull the villagers are! You understand without preaching, but the villagers do not yet understand, though we have been preaching to them every day for a year!"

" In truth, faith, too, is given by Amida. It is beyond human power. This is what we call the miracle of the Vow," said Shinran.

Just then Shoshin-bo came back from without.

" Saibutsu-bo, Saibutsu-bo," he called aloud from the garden. " The bamboo has taken root in the ground! How strange! The bamboo has taken root!"

Saibutsu-bo ran out.

" Really, it has taken root, and has new buds. What a strange thing to see!"

Shinran, hearing it, prostrated himself before the altar and recited the Nembutsu. " How thankful I am for this is a sign that our preaching will be a success."

The chanting of the Nembutsu began in unison spontaneously.

Shinjuro was overjoyed to see this wonder. " Now that my faith has been established, I will lead the villagers into the Nembutsu without fail. They are narrow-minded, like the frog in the well. So they do not follow you. They distrust you as strangers from another land."

" Nothing can be done unless the opportunity comes."

Hearing of the miracle of the bamboo, the villagers gradually began to heed the preaching.

This bamboo became two the following year when it produced a shoot. The next year more shoots grew, and now the place has become a grove of purple bamboo. This is the orign of the temple Jokoji of Toyano.

Shinran spent three years at Toyano.

Having thoroughly learned here the necessity of patience in spreading the teaching, Shinran was ready to tour the province of Hitachi in the east, in accordance with his spiritual destiny.

Chapter 23

PREACHING IN THE EASTERN DISTRICTS

Miyoshi Tamenori, who led Makabe County at Kojima, Hitachi Province, had heard about the teaching of the Easy Path of the ' Other Power,' and had long wished to have the Shonin make a preaching tour in the eastern districts. He sent a messenger to Shinran.

" In the eastern districts," said the messenger, " Kumagai Rensho-bo and Tsuda Nyudo have passed away, and since then we have had no one to guide us in the Nembutsu. The faith in the Nembutsu, which had taken root with much trouble, has gradually died out, and now is nearly forgotten.

" Leader Miyoshi greatly grieves to see this, and is trying very hard to spread the Nembutsu teaching in the eastern districts. You have been in the Echigo district for over seven years, widely planting the seeds of the Nembutsu. So now I beg you to take pity on the rustic people of the east, who have not yet come in contact with Buddhism, and come to preach to them."

Being moved by the earnest invitation, Shinran left

Toyano in the early spring of the second year of Kenpo (1214), walking on the snow that remained on the ground.

Miyoshi Tamenori built a house of worship for Shinran and his party. He had followed Shinran's wishes and built it like an ordinary home with the ridges a little higher than those of ordinary dwellings.

" The place for the preaching of the Nembutsu among the people should not be different from the homes of the people," said Shinran always. He did not like pretentious structures for temples.

He wanted to assimilate himself with the people, to become one with the living and the feelings of the lay-men. This desire of his became stronger as time passed and as he associated with the villagers. If he had lacked the earnest desire to spread the teachings, he would have become a layman himself.

Owing to Tamenori's devotion, more people came to listen to the sermons, not only from Makabe County, but also from Yuki, Okada and Sarushima of the pro-vince of Shimofusa across the river Kinugawa.

Saibutsu-bo and Shoshin-bo had to make trips to preach in place of their teacher, so they could not look after Shinran. Tamenori instructed his daughter Asa-hime to attend to the teacher day and night, and to take care of his things.

One day when Shinran finished his sermon, a samurai came up to the teacher, pushing his way through the audience.

" I have a favor to ask of the Shonin," he said.

" Is there some doubt that you want explained? "

" No, Shonin, I am Kojiro Shigehide, second son of Hatakeyama Shigetada.   In the second year of Gen-kyu (1205) my elder brother Shigeyasu died a violent death at Yuigahama, and my father Shigetada also died at Tsurugamine, shot by an arrow.   Seeing such warriors of peerless loyalty fall victims to slander and die violant deaths, I could not help but realize the uncertainty of life.

" I went to Togano-o and studied the teachings of the Kegon School for several years.   But sad to say, I was of the warrior class and knew little of learning. Moreover, owing to my inherent dullness, I was unable to attain enlightenment.   So I left Togano-o and came back to my home in the east.   There I performed memorial services for my father and brother.   Then I traveled about the country sadly visiting different temples.

" Today I happened to hear your sermon, and felt as if the sun were clearing away dark clouds.   Nothing can compare with my happiness now.

" Would you kindly make me one of your followers and grant me your guidance?   This is the greatest desire of my life."

The honest and sincere eastern warrior implored Shinran with tears.

Shinran sympathized with him.   He gave him the Buddhist name of Josho-bo, and kindly taught him the teaching of the Nembutsu of the ' Other Power.'

It was during this period that the Great Councilor

Nobuaki of Yoshida, Satake Kanja Hideyoshi, and others were converted.

Shinran stayed here for three years and found many devout followers. But he thought that it was harmful to stay long in one place. And so, with the passing of Miyoshi Tamenori into the Pure Land, he moved to the hermitage at Inada in the fifth year of Kenpo (1217).

Asahime, now alone after losing her father, continued to wait on Shinran and accompanied him.

Inada was a secluded spot, with Mt. Kuwagara to the northwest and the Wagakuni Range to the southeast.

Inada Kuro Yorishige was very glad that Shinran had come to stay and preach there. His uncle Utsunomiya Yoritsuna who had been Honen Shonin's follower and known as Shinjitsu-bo, was then living in retirement at Nishiyama. Shinran knew this.

When they moved to Inada, delighted priests and laymen of Niiharu and Ibaragi visited the meeting house. The Nembutsu teaching gradually spread all over Hitachi Province.

It was at this time that Bennen, the Yamabushi[1] monk of the Shugendo sect was converted.

One day Shinran, on his way back from a sermon at Kakioka, had to pass a ridge of the Itajiki mountains.

Bennen came down from the practice floor on the mountain top and hid himself in a grove with his followers, as previously arranged. They waited for Shinran

[1] Ascetic monk of the Shugendo sect, practicing austerities in the mountains with the purpose of acquiring the art of performing miracles.

to pass.

The monk was in Yamabushi attire, wearing a black hood and a hemp robe, and a pair of eight-corded straw sandals. He carried a sword at his side. His two followers had fixed arrows to their rattan bows. There was an ominous atmosphere.

" Did you hear? " said Bennen, who had been listening tensely. " I hear the sound of the Nembutsu. That can't be the wind. The sinful priest is coming home, reciting the Nembutsu."

" Surely. '. . . Dabutsu, Midabutsu ' he is saying."

" Any minute now! " Bennen warned.

The sound of the Nembutsu echoed and came very near. They had calculated the distance and were ready to shoot their arrows as soon as Shinran appeared. However, the person who appeared was not Shinran, but a monkey trainer with a small monkey on his back. He came up the pass, reciting the Nembutsu and playing with the monkey.

Bennen was angrily disappointed. " Even a monkey trainer is uttering the Nembutsu! No wonder our ascetic practices decline! "

" Let's catch him and ask some questions."

The monks suddenly appeared from among the trees, startling the monkey trainer.

" Where did you come from? " they asked.

" I went to Kakioka on business, and I'm now on my way home."

" Didn't you meet a priest in the pass ? "

" I didn't see anyone. But there are many people in

Kakioka. We heard Shinran Shonin's sermon and there was a big crowd of people in Kakioka. I listened to his sermon, too. I felt so grateful that I came back reciting the Nembutsu. Even a humble monkey trainer like me can be reborn into the Pure Land by reciting the Nembutsu, I hear."

"Didn't you hear that this Shinran Shonin would come back through this pass?"

"Oh, have you come to welcome him? If so, it's useless to wait. He planned to return today, but owing to the county headman's pleas, he decided to stay."

"Be gone!" the Yamabushi monk yelled angrily. "The corrupt fellow has the devil's luck, alright. Now the only way to beat him is by a secret spell."

Bennen returned with his followers to his ceremonial platform on the mountain top, and immediately prepared for esoteric practices.

He enshrined God Mayura[1] on the platform. In the incense burner he had a holy fire for an invocation. He made magical signs with his fingers and uttered an incantation. He continued these performances furiously for seven days and nights.

Finally, looking as evil as a demon, Bennen said, "Well, this will be Shinran's last night alive!"

But his follower, who had been to Inada to spy on Shinran, came back with a puzzled look.

"Shinran had come back from Kakioka safely and was preaching as usual today," he said.

---

[1] Supposed to be the incarnation of the Buddha, and is the object of worship in removing misfortunes in Esoteric Buddhism.

"Damn!" Bennen ground his teeth with resentment. "I, who have mastered the esoteric doctrine of Kongokai and Taizokai, director of Shugendo of the province of Hitachi, have exerted myself to the utmost and followed the formulas. But why are there no results? Is it that God Mayura has forsaken me, or that the Shugendo practices have lost their effect? Now I will chop off Shinran's head, even if I turn into a devil!"

Bennen's followers could only tremble at their teacher's frightening expression.

Bennen raged on saying, "Shinran is not observing Buddhist precepts nor preaching the profound doctrine of the scriptures; he was married, eats meat and rejects the traditional discipline. Why are converts crowding his doors, while my practice hall is deserted? What does this mean? I'll meet Shinran face to face in combat and slaughter him."

He immediately hastened to Inada.

At the meeting house there, devout laymen and priests had gathered around Shinran for religious discussion.

"You hypocritical monk!" A loud cry arose outside the paper sliding doors.

Then, forcing the door open, the raging Bennen appeared in Yamabushi attire, armed with a sword.

Everyone was terrified.

"Where's the hypocrite? Let Shinran come out!" Bennen shouted.

Those around Shinran thought he should hide, fearing something would happen to him. So they said,

" It's a raving, obstinate Yamabushi monk. It would be useless to deal with him, so please hide yourself somewhere."

" No, I don't think that is necessary."

Shinran dressed in a plain robe, went out and calmly confronted Bennen.

Bennen glared at Shinran, his eyes shooting fire, and was very surprised to find an opponent who looked so gentle and mild. He had expected either a terrified, precept-breaking monk, or a lawless, aggressive monk burning with anger. But what he saw was a serene, fatherly, mild-mannered monk. Shinran looked untroubled, as if nothing had happened. His attitude was gentle and fearless; there was no hint of revulsion or condescension.

Bennen did not know what to do in this new situation. He became somewhat ashamed of his aggressive attitude.

" First, will you take off your clogs? " asked Shinran. Bennen had entered the room wearing his clogs.

" What's the main object of the Easy Path of the ' Other Power '? " demanded Bennen, approaching Shinran half-heartedly.

" It's our rebirth into the Pure Land by means of Amida's Vow, for we mortals of the latter days of the Law know our own helplessness."

" Then you are a helpless mortal, aren't you? "

" I cannot help admitting it, sad to say."

" Why do you preach the Law, then, knowing you are helpless? "

" I sympathize with those who equally regret their

helplessness, and preach to them to rely on Amida's power and avoid disappointment. I do this out of sympathy for my fellow beings who are as helpless as I am."

" Then what do you do for those who have power to deliver themselves? "

" Those who have power have their own ways.   Sages and holy men would not ask for our instruction.   I don't preach to those who are gifted or able to understand the Law, to those who can deliver themselves from birth-and-death by their own efforts, concentrating their minds and practicing esoteric discipline."

" Then do you admire the holy men of the Sage's Path? "

" They are born nobler than we are.   How can we help but admire them? "

As he listened to the replies, Bennen felt his temper gradually cool.

" Then the Buddha has more mercy on those who deliver themselves with their own power and less mercy on those who are delivered by the ' Other Power,' doesn't He? "

" That is not so," Shinran said firmly.   " Those who are gifted have no doubt received more grace from the Buddha than those followers of the ' Other Power.'

" But in the teaching of the Pure Land School, those believers of the ' Other Power ' receive everything from the Buddha, just like the infant, who receives everything from its mother.   The parent loves the intelligent child and the dull child equally.

" After all, the comparative virtues of self-power and ' Other Power ' depend on the receiver and the time. The deliverance by self-power is suited to those who are gifted; but the deliverance by the ' Other Power ' is suited to those who are not gifted. In the periods of Shobo and Zobo (the first 1,500 years after Sakyamuni), the deliverance by self-power was superior, but in the period of Mappo (to 10,000 years after Shobo and Zobo), the deliverance by the ' Other Power' is superior. This is in accordance with the Buddha's teachings, rather than my opinion."

Shinran's reasonable replies left no opening for attack.

Bennen was silent for some time.

This time Shinran made a searching inquiry: " Has your deliverance been established beyond doubt by means of your esoteric practices of the Shugendo doctrine? "

Bennen wanted to say, " Of course," but could not do so, due to the decline of Shugendo.

Shinran grasped the other's feeling at a glance but did not reprove him.

" I myself was not a follower of the ' Other Power ' from the beginning," he said. " I had been following the ways of deliverance by self-power until I was twenty-nine. I performed meditation and esoteric practices and assiduously studied the teachings of Tendai and Kegon Schools. But sad to say, I could not attain deliverance. I was filled with grief and disappointment, and thought I might as well die.

" It was then that I met Honen Shonin. I immediately gave in, admitting my helplessness and became a follower of the Great Path of the Easy Practice.

" Therefore, I haven't the least intention to deprecate self-effort. I realize I am helpless. In these latter days of the Law, towns and districts are filled with helpless mortals. How can they be delivered from birth-and-death, except by the doctrine of the ' Other Power '?

" If you could pity them and overlook my preachings, it would delight not only me, but Amida, who made the Eighteenth Vow."

Bennen could not get angry at Shinran's straight-forward replies. A horn can combat a horn, but not a spring breeze. Besides, Shinran's gentle words struck at Bennen's weakest point.

" A practice that cannot deliver one from birth-and-death had no importance," Bennen admitted to himself. He, who was originally simple and emotional, but not black-hearted, was quick to get angry and quick to repent.

" This gentle fellow is not to be blamed. And yet, I had intended to kill him! " he thought. He was now filled with remorse.

" I, who intended to hinder the Eighteenth Vow of the Compassionate Amida, and slandered the great Law, am indeed the worst sinner," he realized.

He threw down his sword and sat meekly in front of Shinran.

" I, Bennen, arrogant and wicked, have made an attempt to kill you, who are innocent. I have no excuse to make before the Buddha for the evil I have done. I wish you would cut off my head."

Shinran replied, " Please stand up. I don't know about other sects, but in our sect we make no inquiry about good or evil; people are all equally sinful and yet equally the Buddha's children. As there is no evil that can put aside Amida's Vow, your fault has been forgiven. Wicked people are the very ones to whom the teaching of the ' Other Power ' is open. How could we injure them?

" As for me, I do not seek after goodness; for there is no goodness superior to the Nembutsu. It is most important to utter the Nembutsu and be delivered, leaving everything else as it is. Our main teaching is only this, and nothing else."

Bennen wept deeply. He said, " The profound meaning of rebirth into the Pure Land by the ' Other Power ' has been deeply engraved in my mind. I realize now that the effects of good or evil within our hearts can lead the way to our rebirth into the Pure Land. What need is there for the roundabout way of Shugendo practices? I will follow the Nembutsu doctrine from this very day. Will you accept me as a follower? "

" No, I do not have a single follower. Faith is given by Amida, not by me. And unlike other sects, ours has no scriptures and commentaries that must be learned. As we are all ignorant mortals, we are all common followers of the Nembutsu."

" Then will you let me join the followers of the Nembutsu? "

" That is easily done.   We shall recite the Nembutsu together from now on."

Bennen took off his black hood and robe.   He was given the name Myoho-bo, and became one of the residents of the meeting house.

Chapter 24

THE ESTABLISHMENT OF THE
SHIN SECT

To Shinran, the period of his life at Inada was the most active and happiest from a worldly point of view.

At his back were defenders of his religion and converts such as the county chieftain and temple supporters; to the meeting house came a continuous stream of devout priests and laymen.

His fame and teachings had spread, not only over the entire province of Hitachi, but also over the provinces of Kozuke and Shimofusa.

Among his converts were warriors, merchants, Shinto priests, and even Yamabushi monks.

At home his faithful wife Asahime served him, and his two children, Zenran and Iyanyo, were growing up in good health.

" Though it was an austere life, priests and laymen believers continually called at the door; though the gate was closed, the streets were filled with people, rich and poor. The purpose of spreading Buddhism was accomplished, and the long-cherished desire to benefit all beings was satisfied."[1]

Such were the conditions. It seemed as if Shinran's banner of victory were fluttering over the meeting house. This encouragement led Shinran to establish a new sect called Shinshu in the third year of Jo-o (1224).

This was because Honen Shonin had been dead for a long time, and many of his followers had made faulty interpretations of his teachings. A follower like Sho-kaku Hoin, for instance, had even written a book called *Yuishinsho* in defense of Honen's true motives. Shinran was greatly moved when he read the book.

Shinran was confident that he was the rightful successor to Honen Shonin's faith. Since other followers were making different interpretations and claiming to be the true successors, Shinran had no choice but to organize a new sect in order to distinquish his views from the others.

Due to these circumstances, the establishment of the Shinshu sect was proclaimed at the meeting house at Inada.

In the center of the altar was placed the image of Amida. On its left was a portrait of Prince Shotoku; and on its right, that of Honen Shonin. The display was pure and solemn in spirit.

Incense burned continuously on the altar, and the candlelight seemed to symbolize the everlasting light of the sect. The chirping of the " scripture-chanting bird " (the Japanese nightingale) echoed in the clear air

[1] A quotation from *Kudensho*, a chronicle of Shinran's sayings and accomplishments, compiled by Kakunyo Shonin.

of the spring morning.

Priests, laymen, and temple supporters, numbering one hundred, sat in orderly lines. Those who sat[1] facing the altar were Zensho Shonin, the eldest disciple, Inada Kuro Yorishige and his son Kyonen, Sainen-bo of Noda, Shosho-bo of Inugai, Zeshin-bo of Waga, Shin-en-bo of Hikone, Nyushin-bo of Anazawa, Doen-bo of Uchida, Ren-i-bo of Shimotsuma, Shingan-bo of Awa, Junshin-bo of Kashima, Myoho-bo of Narahara, Nengan-bo of Okube, and others. It appeared that all the most respected Buddhists had gathered here.

Then the bell rang, announcing the opening of the ceremony. All sat up straight, adjusted their robes, and clasped their hands in veneration.

From the corridor on the right appeared Shoshin-bo, reverently holding up something wrapped in silk.

Then came Shinran, followed by Saibutsu-bo. After them appeared Asahime in a flowing robe and red skirt, together with Zenran and Iyanyo, also finely dressed. They sat in the seats provided for them.

Shinran clasped his hands respectfully and worshipped before the altar, then sat on a platform. Immediately all began to chant " Namu-Amida-Butsu " in unison. The sound of the chanting that filled the hall sounded bright and hopeful, like the rising of the spring tide.

Shoshin-bo unwrapped the scroll and read it aloud. It was the proclamation of a new sect:

" I, Shinran the Ignorant, on the night of April 4

---

[1] The seats in front of the altar were the best and supposed to be occupied by those of high rank.

in the third year of Kennin, received in my dream the merciful Kannon's message, which came true.   I hereby establish the Jodo Shinshu Sect, so that not only I myself can have faith in the Great Vow of Amida, but in order that I can let others know of it.

" My former teacher Honen Shonin, in consideration of his fellow beings in the latter days of the Buddha's Law, upheld the Great Vow of the ' Other Power ' and preached the teaching by which common mortals can make an entrance straight into the Pure Land.

" However, the Shonin has passed away, and since that time a number of wrong interpretations and heretical views have appeared, and rigthteousness has nearly been overthrown. Nothing could be more deplorable. " Stupid though I am, I received my instructions direct from my teacher and have followed his true intentions always.   It is in order to reveal these that I have established the sect called Jodo Shinshu (the true sect of the Jodo school).   As the basic material for the new sect, the *Kyogyoshinsho* has been compiled."

All clasped their hands and recited the Nembutsu in chorus.

Shinran had spent five strenuous years in compiling the *Kyogyoshinsho*, the greatest work of his life.   It is a very important book on which the Jodo Shinshu is based, and is the equivalent of Honen Shonin's *Senjaku Hongan Nembutsu-shu*.

In those days holy scriptures were available to very few people.   The eastern districts were lacking in culture, compared to Kyoto, and so Shinran faced many problems.

He did not know what to do at first. At last he called on Inada Yorishige, one of his patrons, and said:

" Since the death of Honen Shonin, the Jodo School is in utter confusion due to differing interpretations. If this state continues, later generations will not know what Honen Shonin's real ideas were. Therefore, I want to write a book called *Kyogyoshinsho* and reveal the truth of Honen Shonin's teaching."

" I think that is exceedingly important," said Yorishige. " I hope you will be able to complete it as soon as possible."

" In writing it, what I need most are the sacred Sutras. I cannot do anything without the *Tripitaka*[1] for reference."

" I have a good idea. The temple Yakushiji of Shimotsuke Province is under the control of the Utsunomiyas, our head-family, so it is not difficult for me to gain access to the archives.

" And as for the Ashikaga Library, its patron Ashikaga Yoshiuji is my relative by marriage, so I will have it opened especially for Shonin's sake."

Shinran rejoiced to receive so much unexpected help. He immediately went to Yakushiji and entered its large archives.

Next he had trouble in procuring writing brushes and paper. He could keep using worn-out brushes, but needed large quantities of paper because a great deal of copying was necessary. Paper of good quality came from distant places such as Kamakura, and it cost

---

[1] A complete collection of the Buddhist scriptures.

a great deal.   Besides, it was almost impossible to collect paper of consistent quality.

" I am completely at a loss about paper," Shinran said with wrinkled brow.

" I will take charge of supplying paper," said Asahime, " so that you can concentrate on your writing.   It's too much for you to search for the paper and, at the same time, do so much copying every day."

" That will help me immensely, but I wonder if you will be able to get paper."

" Please leave it to me," she answered comfortingly.

Asahime searched for writing paper in the neighboring villages and collected one or two quires.   Sometimes it was sent to her from other districts through her friends, and sometimes, without Shinran's knowledge, she asked patrons of the temple to buy some for her.   She tried every means to provide sufficient quantities.   But as for the quality of paper, no matter how hard she tried, she was unable to keep it uniform.

" I cannot get the same quality of paper, though I do my best," she said.   " You may not like it, but please put up with it for the present."

" That is all right.   I'm satisfied as long as I can have paper," said Shinran.

Sometimes the paper he used was yellow, being remanufactured paper; and other times it would be very coarse on both sides.   If he could not get even these, he used old scraps patched together.

Shinran did not complain.   He was grateful for Asahime's help, and managed to write neatly despite worn-out brushes.

Finally his work was completed. Nothing could compare with his satisfaction. Asahime shed tears, overcome by emotion.

Thus was produced the *Kyogyoshinsho* in six volumes, the basic scripture of the Jodo Shinshu, which is still greatly admired not only by devotees but by scholars as well.

This book is the most important of all Shinran's many writings. In it he has clarified the essence of the Jodo Shinshu with judicious selections, irrespective of fundamental and supplementary Sutras, and without discriminating between the patriarchs. He made free interpretations with the eye of faith. His unique views are evident in his interpretation of the scriptures. Though there are some errors in minor points, they never detract from the whole truth—they rather help to reveal it.

Among specialists in religious doctrines, there are some who try to find fault with the book by indicating errors in words and phrases, or by saying there are omissions. But if one reads it with the inspiration of his own religious experiences, he will find enlightening truths that are unique.

Chapter 25

THE LAST ENDEAVOR

In the spring of the first year of Joei (1232), Shinran had a strange dream.

A mendicant monk in black robe was standing beside a river that looked like the Shinano, earnestly preaching to a peasant with a sheaf of blighted rice in his hand. The peasant went away with a stone-like look. The monk remained standing on the river bank looking sad. Then on the water appeared the Amida of Zenkoji.

The scene suddenly changed, and now the same monk was being entertained in a beautifully decorated room of a wealthy person. A number of priests and laymen were sitting in a row. There were some women in fine clothes among them. When the monk preached, they fell on their knees to bow. The monk then departed in a palanquin, while crowds of people knelt on both sides of the road.

Then there was on a street corner, a picture of a monk with a demon's arms trying to embrace him from behind.

Shinran was startled out of his sleep. He found he was covered with perspiration. The dream remained vividly in his mind.

" I wonder how long I have been in Inada," he thought, then found he had been there for sixteen years. He recalled the words: " We must not stay long at one place." When he first came to the eastern district from Toyano in Echigo, he had not intended to stay long. His preaching visit, which was supposed to be temporary, now seemed permanent. He wondered why.

It had come about so naturally, possibly due to ties in his previous existence; only this could he say.

Life was comfortable here; everything went well; there were good patrons; the teaching spread like fields bending before the wind; a livelihood was no problem; he was respected and praised by many.

Finally the proclamation of a new sect had been made, and a great book had been written. Imposing temples like Senjuji of Takada were erected.

" Then how about my faith and devotion? Have they improved? "

When Shinran thought about it, he felt a chill creep over him. Outwardly he had made a remarkable advance, but not inwardly, he thought. There were indications that he had become accustomed to the life of ease, although it had happened unknowingly and unintentionally.

All the reverence and praise accorded him had set the stage. His attitude had always been a passive one, ready to accept what others wanted him to do, and this together with the circumstances had led him to become the founder of a new sect.

He had not purposely sought for fame or profit; but looking at it objectively, he decided the result was the same as if he had sought them.

As for his relationship to Asahime, could he say definitely that there had been no emotional passion?

There might have been a tendency, after the children were born, to devote himself too much to the easygoing home life.

Moreover, in connection with the stabilization of the order and the opening of new temples, could he say that he had given no thought to the future of his wife and children?

Was it not true, he thought seriously without being self-indulgent, that he was unknowingly walking the path toward spiritual corruption?

Compared to his three years in the deserted village of Toyano, near the river Shinano (where he lacked rice and salt, where there was not a single believer, where he grieved for the ignorant mortals who did not care to understand the Buddha's earnest wish to save them), could he say that his life now was not frivolous?

In the first place, was it fitting for monks, who were likened to floating clouds and running water, to stay and preach at one place for sixteen years?

To deliver people in accordance with one's spiritual destiny could not possibly mean staying in one place and being bound only by certain people's kindness.

Had it not been his ideal, at the very beginning and

when he made his vow at Zenkoji in Shinano, to move from place to place, even if it were a place as nice as the Chinese capitals of Chang-an or Lo-yang?

Twenty years had passed since then, and he was now sixty years old. If he did not make any efforts now, he would never be anything more than a priest striving after fame and fortune.

He now realized he had been standing on the edge of an awful abyss. His dream must have been a warning from the Amida of Zenkoji.

After this event, he began to wonder night and day how he could change his present life. However, when he tried to do it, he found that it was no easy matter, discovering how he had been captivated strongly by worldly interests.

It happened that Shinbutsu-bo came to see him at this time from the temple Senjuji of Takada with a temple patron of Miyamura.

" The new hall of Senjuji has been completed," said Shinbutsu-bo. " It's the most magnificent temple in the eastern provinces. Governor Ouchi-no-suke of the province, Lord of the Oguri Castle, Lord of the Soma Castle, and Lord Hiratsuka were all very satisfied. And as for the construction of the Sutra archives, which you approved, the master-carpenter Hirota Mitsumasa and fifty other carpenters started work on the 25th of this month."

Shinran was deep in thought, but made fitting replies.

" Lord Tachibana Motokazu of Kasama Castle has recently contributed to build the bell tower," Shinbutsu-bo continued. "And we want to collect contributions from among the patrons and followers of the temple, to found a large bell suitable for the tower. So I have accompanied some supporters here today."

"I thank you for your efforts," said Shinran. "We have already collected large contributions for the main temple, the archives, and other buildings, so I don't think we should seek further contributions from them."

Shinbutsu-bo looked somewhat dissatisfied. "You are right," he said, "but since Lord Tachibana has contributed for the bell tower, I'm afraid of what people would think if we did not have a bell suitable for the tower."

"We must have a bell, but it is not necessary to provide a large one. An ordinary bell would be sufficient."

"We want to have one as large as possible, for it is going to transmit the teaching of the Shin Sect day and night to the followers far and near."

"In the different hamlets and villages there are many poor people. They have already contributed much hard labor in raising the ground, carrying stones, and other services in the erection of Senjuji. So I think we should not ask them for further contributions for the time being."

The patron of Miyamura Village drew closer and said, "Shonin, we understand, so we shall not collect contributions from the followers at large, but only from the patrons. Will you please allow us to do this?"

"I thank the parishioners for their contributions

time and again. However, it is not desirable to depend wholly on rich gifts in the construction of a Buddhist house of worship. We should collect small donations from many persons. There is a story about a Zen monk who made a pilgrimage and collected one roof tile from each contributor to reconstruct a temple which had gone to ruin."

The patron drew back, looking dissatisfied. The visitors were discouraged.

Shinbutsu-bo looked perplexed and said, " Then we will go back to Takada to discuss the matter, and come back again."

" I thank you all for your kindness. Remember: temples and buildings are secondary; preaching is primary."

" I understand that. The Shinshu Sect is established, and Senju Amidaji has been erected. Now we want to crown it with perfection, to give the finishing touch to the work. I hope you will think about it."

When Shinbutsu-bo and the patrons had gone, some attractive fishes arrived from the manager of a fishermen's group in Kasumigaura. A large dish of beautiful fresh carp of black and red, sliced and arranged artistically, was placed on a gold-lacquered tray decorated with a dwarf tree.

The messenger said, " I was told to deliver this in celebration of Master Zenran's birthday. For several days it had been stormy at Kasumigaura, and the fishermen were having a hard time. But today we caught some beautiful carp so we prepared and brought them."

Shinran, who had been looking at the dish, was filled with discomfort. He was grateful for the gift, but it was so extravagant! This would be suitable for a provincial governor or a millionaire. He compared the fishermen, suffering due to the stormy weather, to himself and his family eating this delicacy. What would become of his children if they grew up in such conditions?

Moreover, he himself was a monk. Though he did not mind eating meat and fish, this was not food to stave off hunger, but extravagance gone to extremes. Was this life in accordance with the spirit of mercy?

Shinran could not help feeling that the atmosphere around him was far from that of religious devotion.

Just then Asahime entered.

" My, what a beautiful dish of carp! "

Shinran was silent.

" Who brought it? "

" It was sent from the fishermen's manager at Kasumigaura in honor of Zenran's birthday."

" Oh, really? " She looked happy. " A splendid dish! I will put it in the alcove."

" Where is Zenran? " Shinran asked.

" He went to the archery court with Iyanyo."

" He's fond of military sports, isn't he? "

" He'll change as he grows up, I think," she said.

" I feel uneasy about the future of a child who is given such luxurious things."

" What do you mean? " asked Asahime with wide,

wondering eyes.

" Well, a man will not attain perfection if he does not undergo hardships in his childhood. If he becomes accustomed to luxury and service, I'm afraid of what Karma retributions he will have to undergo."

" I try to avoid luxury, but many followers contribute various gifts. As a result, we live in comfort, though I know it is not good for the children."

Asahime bent down her head remorsefully.

" It is natural that you know nothing of poverty, being a daughter of a county chieftain and having a carefree upbringing. But a human being cannot be called mature unless he suffers poverty once."

' No matter how poor I may become, it would make no difference to me. I have no craving to live in comfort."

She was being as honest as possible, under the circumstances, Shinran thought.

After this incident, Shinran realized more and more that his present surroundings did not encourage religious devotion. He decided he had been tainted by his surroundings, and blamed himself for staying a long time at one place.

On August 6 of that year, Shinran at last arrived at a final decision. He made a vow to the Buddha that he would leave Inada and resume the life of a wandering priest, regardless of any personal difficulties.

He summoned his principal followers and explained his resolution to start on a pilgrimage.

They were all astounded. They thought that Shinran

had made up his mind to stay in the eastern districts.

Junshin-bo of Kashima was hard to convince. He said, " This is a complete surprise to us. We thought Shonin was going to live here permanently, for the Jodo Shinshu Sect was founded in this temple, and the Senju Amidaji of Takada has been built. But now we learn that you intend to go on a pilgrimage. We are very bewildered."

Shinran felt ashamed of himself and said, " It is understandable that you should say so, Junshin-bo. I had been careless, and had thought as you did. I moved here from Echigo, resolving at first not to stay long. However, I must have had spiritual influences from a previous existence, for devout priests and laymen gradually gathered here. I felt at home, and forming further ties, I finally spent sixteen years here.

" This summer, however, I dreamed of the Amida of Zenkoji, who gave me a warning. This was because I had been neglecting my duty, forgetting my original vow and stayed here for such a long time, being overcome by people's kindness. I was from the beginning a wandering priest. I understand your perplexity, but I want to fulfill my original vow and start on a pilgrimage."

Sainen-bo of Noda shed tears and said, " I am only a mediocre priest of unstable faith. I have relied on you, Shonin, hoping to hear your preaching always. If you leave us now, it will be like losing a light in the darkness. I do not know of the past, but you have reached an advanced age, and a pilgrimage would be so strenuous; please give up this idea."

Shinran wept silently.

Nyushin-bo of Anazawa looked as if he were utterly lost.

" My village is like a fort, dependent on this base at Inada as the inner citadel. If the citadel is vacant, our temple and groups of followers will fall to pieces."

Shinran raised his voice and said, " That is exactly the harm of staying long in one place. You are showing signs of relying on me, rather than on the Law. If I had not come here, you would have relied only on the Nembutsu. If you think that the Law and groups of followers would fall to pieces after I leave, then this is a harmful effect of my staying here too long. The deliverer is Amida, and the only thing to rely on is the Law. Hearing what you say, I realize more than ever the necessity of going on a pilgrimage."

Shinran's determination was firm.

" If you go on a pilgrimage," said Raiju-bo of Inada uneasily, " what are you going to do with this meeting house in Inada? "

" I should like to entrust it to Zensho Shonin, who has the highest rank. As for Senjuji in Takada, I will ask Saibutsu-bo to take charge.

" I have stayed here too long, and the resulting harm has accumulated everywhere, causing problems for all. This, I regret, is all due to my Karma effects.

" But if I remain here, I shall be committing more sins; please forgive my faults and accept my reasons for going on a pilgrimage."

Hearing Shinran speak so reasonably, his disciples and followers could not ask him to reconsider, and so they just wept in utterly disappointed silence.

That night Asahime said to Shinran, " You have good reason to go on a pilgrimage, but the vow you made was nineteen years ago. Now you are advanced in years. I cannot help feeling uneasy about your wandering." She looked pale.

" Don't worry. I am strong, as you can see. Great priests of ancient days all devoted themselves to discipline until they were eighty or ninety years old. I am sixty yet; I am not so old that I must remain idle."

Asahime was discouraged. " Being a woman, I cannot accompany you on your trip. How should I go on living? "

" I have asked the Inadas, both father and son, to look after you," said Shinran, holding back his tears. " I will ask Zensho Shonin to do the same. Since you are familiar with this district, I hope you will stay here and bring up the children.

" I'm sure you are prepared. Our pledges are only for this temporary world. Thanks to a strong bond of a previous existence, we were able to live together in the same house for nineteen years. There are many who are bound by fate for only two or three years.

" It does not mean that I am leaving this world. I will write to you. Besides, the children will help to divert your mind. If you miss me, please recite ' Namu-Amida-Butsu,' and you will feel close to me."

Shinran spoke carefully and comforted her.

Asahime controlled herself and said, " I will take charge of the house while you are away.   Not knowing when we shall meet again, I would like you to perform the ordination rites which I have long desired."

" Certainly, I will perform the rites for you."

Shinran had been refusing her requests to be tonsured, but now he thought it was appropriate, and so he shaved her hair.   He gave her the Buddhist name, " Eshinni."

Shinran gazed at his wife, a beautiful nun, and wondered when he would see her again.   It was the day before his departure.

When the followers learned that Shinran was going to leave Inada, they all lamented.   They stood on both sides of the road to see him depart, and everyone wept like an infant who had to leave his mother.

Among others, Saibutsu-bo won people's pity.   At the declining age of seventy-six, he could not go with Shinran.

The latter had told him to return to his home town of Shiratori in Shinano Prefecture, and take charge of the temple.

His eyes filled with tears, Saibutsu-bo said, " All of you, please listen.   Surely I shall be forsaken by my guardian Bodhisattva, Kanjizai.   I first met the Shonin on Mount Hiei, and since I was forty years old, I have been always by his side, like a shadow.

" I followed him from Echigo to Shinano, and from Kojima to Inada.   But I have grown old and infirm, as you see, and cannot accompany the Shonin on his tour. I have been told to go back to my home town and preach." He wept loudly.

Shinran had determined to end all his personal ties and was holding back his tears.

He bore his heartbreak by reciting the Nembutsu, and left his home, the village of Inada.

To the devout men and women who stood along the roads and in the fields, from the house of worship to Fubukidani, Shinran expressed thanks for their kindness for sixteen years, and bade them farewell forever in his heart.

Chapter 26

THE PARTING AT LAKE ASHI-NO-KO

Shinran traveled from Kamakura to Oiso and then to Kozu. And in the autumn of the first year of Bunreki (1234), he was in the Hakone mountains, accompanied by Shoshin-bo and Kenchi-bo.

It was night and the moon was shining when they left Yumoto.

Shinran suggested that they might walk through the difficult 20-mile pass, viewing the moon.

They made their preparations and started to climb the mountain path. But the crossing was no easy matter. By the time they came to the Futago Pass, Shinran was exhausted and Shoshin-bo had to push him from the back.

" I'm an old man now," said Shinran.

No matter how brave his spirit might be, his physical strength was fading, he realized.

He recalled Saibutsu-bo, who had wept and said, " How miserable it is to become old!" Shinran could not ignore his physical decline, which was already making his tour difficult.

When they were resting at Ashi-no-ko, after spending the night at Hakone Gongen, Shinran said to Shoshin-bo:

" You have accompanied me this far, but I must ask you now to go back to Inada."

Shoshin-bo was surprised. " No matter where you went on a pilgrimage—northern Echigo, or Kanto districts—I was always the one who carried your Sutra box. I have made up my mind to accompany you wherever you go, and to see you pass away safely into the Pure Land. Why do you want to forsake me now? I do not understand."

" You have a right to feel as you do.   But I intend to return to the capital."

" Then take me there, please."

" I want you to return to Hitachi, because I have misgivings about affairs at Inada. I have weakened physically so I hardly have a chance to return to Inada. As you know, Inada is closely connected with Buddhism. Above all, I have left Eshinni, Zenran, and Iyanyo there, and I want to ask you, my confidant, to look after them.

" I cannot walk steep paths any more, so it will not be necessary to ask for your attendance from now on.

" In the capital my old acquaintances among the Yoshimizu followers have already scattered, and I may find it difficult to make a living. Besides, I have no intention to organize a religious group; I wish to live alone in seclusion the rest of my life. So I may write to you at Inada for some assistance. I have shared my joys and sorrows with you for thirty-one years, since Honen Shonin put you in my care when you were eighteen years old. No ties from previous existances can be more close.

"I wanted you to accompany me as far as Kyoto, but activities at Inada are constantly troubling my mind. Surely something must have happened there. This is why I am sending you back to Inada. So please be understanding."

Shoshin-bo had been weeping quietly.

"I reverently will obey your request," he said sincerely.

"I am glad you accept my wishes."

"It was selfish to want to be with you. If I can be of any service to you and to the Law, then that would be a proper repayment of my indebtedness. I will go back to Inada, help Zensho-bo, look after the future of the Lady and her children, and help with your living expenses. So please set your mind at rest."

"I'm so happy to hear that. I thank you from the bottom of my heart."

"This may be our final parting. Good-bye."

Shoshin-bo dried his eyes and retraced his steps along the lakeside, frequently looking back.

Shinran could not hold back his tears. He stood gazing until Shoshin-bo disappeared in the mist.

The reeds rustled in the autumn wind, and wild geese crossed the sky.

Chapter 27

IMPERMANENCY

So many years had elapsed that it all seemed hazy and dreamlike to Shinran. Thirty years had passed since he had left the capital in a palanquim as an exile. Honen Shonin had been dead for twenty-four years. Kumagai Rensho-bo, Kua, Shinku, and Chosai—those followers of Honen Shonin at Yoshimizu—had also died one after another. Ryukan Risshi, who wrote *Kensenjaku* and fought against Mount Hiei, was also gone.

The Emperor and ex-Emperor of the Yoshimizu prohibition period had fallen from power after the Shokyu Revolt. The Genji clan had lost its strength, and now it was the Hojo clan that held sway over the country.

Lady Tamahi and Lord Kanezane were also gone, their graves covered with moss. Saibutsu-bo, who followed Shinran's palanquin out of the capital, had retired i_ Shiratori in Shinano province. As for Shoshin-bo, Shinran had parted from him at Hakone.

Shinran could not find a single old acquaintance in the capital; those who walked the streets were all strangers.

Was this his home city?

Shinran walked the main thoroughfares of the capital, but no one took any notice of the plain old man.

The young girls in beautiful attire who walked along the streets had not been born when he was here decades ago.

Years had rolled by, and nearly everything had changed, except for the mountains and rivers, Amida's earnest desire to save mankind, and Shinran's own Karma effects.

He wished to devote the rest of his life to the realization of Amida's great compassion and his own Karma effects. This was his greatest wish for his last years. For twenty-five years he had devoted his life, to the best of his ability, in spreading the Buddhist teachings among his fellow men.

During the years of self-sacrifice, he had had no time to think about himself and his well-being. His spirit had run dry, and his intellectual ability worn away.

He thought he would like to spend the rest of his life all alone, filled with gratitude for Amida's great benevolence. He did not care for fame or fortune; the Order, too, was troublesome. He only wished to be alone with Amida.

In his spare moments he thought he would like to write simple Wasan.[1] If he should suffer from lack of food or clothing, he would ask his old followers in Kanto for help. If that were impossible, he would stand on

[1] Hymns.

Shijo or Gojo Bridge and beg for alms.

He went from place to place to live. Sometimes he stayed at Gojo Nishi-no-toin, and sometimes at Sanjo Tomi-no-koji, or in a humble hut in Okazaki, or at the temple Zenpo-in at Matenokoji.

During his last years he completely escaped the adoration and reverence that had characterized his life at Inada. No longer surrounded and idolized, he was able to become his own self again.

It was probably this life that gave such intensity to his inner light of faith. This profound faith described in *Tannisho*,[1] written by Yuien-bo, was the result of his life in these last years. His life was extremely simple, with the bare necessities provided through money from his Kanto followers.

The true devotion of the Jodo Shinshu life of faith— to rejoice at Amida's great compassion while living one's Karma-bound daily life—was clearly demonstrated.

His last years in the capital were brilliant and vital ones that gave to Jodo Shinshu the latent lustre that brightened in later generations. His years of preaching at Inada alone could not have accomplished this.

He exchanged letters with his Kanto followers, received donations and reports and was consulted about various matters.

Correspondence being inconvenient in those days, he gradually lost contact with his lesser acquaintances. Only those who were closely connected with him

[1] English translation is available.

spiritually continued to correspond with him.

After Shinran's departure, there were many difficulties in the religious circles in Inada, Takada and other places in Kanto. The groups lacked the brilliance of former times, and their solidarity was lost.

Due to agitation among the followers, the lives of Eshinni, Zenran, and Iyanyo gradually became uneasy and uncomfortable as they were dragged into the currents of disturbances.

However, a few followers still continued warm relations with Shinran even after his return to the capital, although they lived far away.

Once when Shinran lived at Gojo Nishi-no-toin, these friends came to call on him, fulfilling their long-cherished desire.

Meeting after a long separation, teacher and disciples took each other's hands and shed tears of joy.

"Shonin, you have grown old, too, haven't you?"

"You, too, have changed beyond recognition since I saw you last in Inada."

"But we are glad to see you in good health."

"How are things in the east?"

"There are difficulties, but those who have strong faith are still united and living up to the teachings."

A layman who felt nostalgic about the days said, "But those days when you were there will never come back again. Those were the best days."

They all thought sadly of the days when Shinran was in Inada.

"I hear that Myoho-bo passed away into the Pure

Land. He had a violent temper, and I still remember vividly the time when he was converted."

Myokyo-bo leaned forward and said, " I was his follower since the time he was a Yamabushi. His disposition did not change after he embraced the faith of the Nembutsu. In his last moments he recited the Nembutsu several hundred times very loudly. He surely must have attained rebirth of the highest degree in the Pure Land."

" We have not many years to live. We, too, would like to attain rebirth of the highest degree."

" Well, Shonin," said one of the followers, " nearly ten years have passed since we parted at Inada. You, no doubt, have given yourself up to devotions since you came here, so you must have deepened your faith. Since we have come here from Hitachi and Shimofusa, crossing the borders of more than ten provinces, please give us an interpretation of your faith so that we can share it later with those at home."

Shinran answered simply, " My faith is the same as that which I preached to you at Inada ten years ago."

" But years have passed since then. Moreover, it was your desire to put your heart into your devotions that made you leave Inada. Therefore, there must have been considerable progress in your faith."

Shinran said with a serious look, " No. My faith has not changed at all."

The followers all looked incredulous.

" Please listen, all of you," said Shinran sharply. " There is nothing in the Jodo Shinshu faith except to recite the Nembutsu and be delivered by Amida. Even if we devote ourselves to this for ten years or a hundred years, we cannot add anything else to our faith, since it is given to us by Amida, and is not of our making. The moment we decide to recite the Nembutsu, feeling assured that we will attain rebirth into the Pure Land by the power of Amida's wonderful Vow, we will be embraced by Amida's light and never be forsaken. There is nothing else I can add to this, no matter how many years I devote myself to the teachings.

" I heard from Honen Shonin at Yoshimizu the teaching of rebirth into the Pure Land by means of the Nembutsu, and became convinced. Forty years have passed since then, but I have not added anything to it.

" If you desire to hear something more than this, there are a number of famous teachers at Nara and Hiei. If you think that I have acquired a different doctrine here in the capital, you are greatly mistaken.

" There is only this single-minded faith and nothing else. And there is no difference between one person's faith and another person's. In this uniformity lies the rock-like solidity of the Jodo Shinshu faith.

" Faith is not mastered by a person; it is given by Amida. Therefore, it is unchangeable—everywhere—forever.

" If there is such a thing as progress in one's faith in Jodo Shinshu, it is to become more single-minded and sincere—not seeking anything else, but completely becoming one with the single thought of the Nembutsu."

The followers were all still. Shinran's serene faith in the Nembutsu had captured their hearts.

A young layman then said, " I was a child when Shonin was in Inada. My father, who died some years ago, was a devout believer in the Nembutsu. I heard from my father about the rebirth into the Pure Land by reciting the Nembutsu, but there is one thing I do not understand. Where can we find the proof that if we utter the Nembutsu we can be reborn into the Pure Land? When I asked my father, he only said that he believed what he heard from Shinran Shonin. I have not been able to rid myself of this doubt. Will you please tell me? "

Shinran said seriously, " Like your father, I only believe what Honen Shonin has said. In the first place, there is no proof in regard to faith. If you seek proof, you do not have faith.

" If Amida's Vow is true, Sakyamuni's teahings cannot be untrue. If Sakyamuni's teachings are true, Zendo's commentaries cannot be untrue. If Zendo's Commentaries are true, Honen Shonin's teachings cannot be untrue."

After Shinran said this, he thought for some time. Then he continued, shaking his head.

" No, even if I were deceived by Honen Shonin and went to hell, I would not feel resentful; for I was a sinner from the beginning, and had no chance of going elsewhere except hell. Supposing I thought I could attain the Pure Land through special practices, I would feel bitter if I were deceived.

" But this is beyond my power, and I was from the start bound for hell. To tell the truth, I do not know whether the Nembutsu is a seed by which I can be reborn into the Pure Land, or a force that will cast me to hell. I leave everything in the hands of Amida—my hope, my life, I myself. He can take me wherever he pleases."

Tears fell from the young man's eyes.

"I understand now. I understand I was conceited. Now I know for the first time what faith means. My father could not explain well, but he surely had faith."

All the believers realized that they had never heard the Shonin tell his thoughts so frankly, and knew that their faith fell far short of his.

Seeing that his visitors were very tense, Shinran smiled and said, " My talk has become too serious. The point is this: just rely on the Amida Buddha like a child. Please make yourselves comfortable."

And he made fresh tea for them with his own hands.

An old follower gazed around the room and said, " You probably find it bothersome morning and evening, living all by yourself."

" I feel at peace in my old age. While I was in Inada, I was surrounded by many respectful people and lived in great comfort. Now I like this simple life."

But Shinran's life with a single attendant was more than simple. They could clearly see poverty.

" If there are things you need, please tell us."

" I thank you all for always helping me with your donations."

" We can do little; moreover the east is remote and correspondence is very inconvenient."

Then they all talked about their home towns and various other subjects.

But they hesitated to talk about Eshinni or Zenran or Iyanyo. For Zenran, who had an ambitious spirit, had expressed heretical views, contrary to his father's teachings, and had agitated the followers. Consequently, he had fallen into disgrace with his father. Iyanyo, who was beautiful and unsophisticated, had the weakness of being too emotional and losing the proper course. This conduct troubled her mother Eshinni, who was also worried by financial problems.

The visitors finally said good-bye, feeling the sorrow of parting.

" I wonder when we can see each other again."

" We shall meet in the Pure Land. Don't forget your Nembutsu," said Shinran.

" We will feel close to you always in the Nembutsu."

" Take good care of yourselves on your way home."

" Thank you very much, Shonin. Take good care of yourself."

Shinran stood at the gate to watch.

The followers looked back time and again, knowing this was their last parting, and disappeared among the people in the streets.

Chapter 28

FATHER AND SON

It was, of course, unusual for a priest to marry and have children. Since social life was usually governed by certain manners and customs, such a life would be subject to contradictions.

Shinran's marriage had broken a long established custom. Had he given up his priesthood and recited the Nembutsu as a layman, there would not have been any trouble. But the difficulty was that he wore a priest's black robe and performed priestly duties.

Since Shinran was anxious to preach, he had to fulfill a preacher's role in society. Otherwise people would have been dissatisfied.

We still have similarly troublesome contradictions today, so in Shinran's days his situation must have been very difficult.

Zenran was born of a marriage under such circumstances and he grew up in this atmosphere. The contradictions obviously were reflected in Zenran's nature; and for this he could not be wholly blamed.

After all, this was an effect of Shinran's Karma and

the founding of the radically new religion called Jodo Shinshu.

Shinran realized this as he spent his later life in self-examination.

In his heart he must have felt pity for Zenran and must have been filled with remorse.

In childhood Zenran was full of pep and fond of military sports.   He had great influence among children, for his father was famous not only in Hitachi but in all the eastern provinces, and was respected and admired even by governors of the provinces and other influencial people in the Inada district.

Zenran's ambitious spirit was gradually intensified. When he was a child he attended the splendid proclamation ceremony of the founding of Jodo Shinshu, and saw many priests and laymen regarding his father as a living Buddha.

Such things encouraged his conceit and no doubt caused his arrogance.   Then too his life was for years a carefree one.

Suddenly his father announced that he was going away, leaving his wife and children.   Zenran did not understand why his father was doing this.   He saw his mother growing pale and losing her appetite.

When he was about to go to the archery court with a friend, his mother said sadly, " Please don't go today. Don't go anywhere today.   Please stay by my side."

" Mother, what is the matter? "

Zenran looked into her face, trembling.   His younger sister Iyanyo clung to her mother, not knowing anything.

" Father is going far away on a pilgrimage."

" What is a pilgrimage? "

" He is going on a trip to a distant place."

" And when is he coming home? "

The mother wept again.

" We don't know when he will come back."

" Then why can't you and Iyanyo and I go with him, too? "

" Because women and children cannot go on a pilgrimage."

Zenran and Iyanyo burst out crying. The mother embraced the two children and said, " Please don't leave my side. I feel so lonely."

The father came home from a visit. He looked serious. The children were afraid of him because he had been looking so serious recently.

The father was displeased when he saw them.

The mother pushed the children aside.

" What sort of behavior is this? What happened to your resolutions? "

Asahime raised her tear-drenched face and replied, " I am prepared, but when I see the children, I become sad."

" You let the children see your tears, not thinking of the effect on them. I see that your self-discipline has been fruitless."

Seeing Shinran exceedingly displeased, Asahime blushed with shame and said, " Please pardon me. I lost my composure unthinkingly. I will be more careful from now on."

The children stood sadly, looking at their parents.

" Please listen, Asahime.   This is a critical time for me.   I have made a firm decision, despite my obligations to others, severing my connections with friends, in order to fulfill my vow to the Amida of Zenkoji."

Asahime dried her tears, put her hands down in obeisance and said, " It was my mistake; please forgive me. I will not show the children any tears in the future."

Soon after this event the father left Inada.

The children, holding their mother's hands, saw their father's departure.

The father, wearing leggings and a braided hat, looked back once from the bridge and then disappeared.   The mother nearly collapsed.

When she came home she shut herself in a room and wept for a long time.

Zenran became lonely.   His father, compared with fathers of other children, did not seem to care much about his children, and there was something about him which made him hard to appraoch.   Nevertheless, Zenran was very sad after his father's departure.

The boy stood waiting on the bridge every day, but his father did not come back.   The atmosphere within the house changed.

The mother, who had shaved off her hair and had become a nun, began to do the housework, looking melancholy as if she had resigned herself to her fate. But her conduct was hard to understand.

" When is father coming back? " Zenran asked her one day.

" He is serving the Buddha in the Buddha's country. He will come back when his work is over."

Her answer meant little to Zenran. He feared his father might never come back.

Months glided by.

Changes occurred in the meeting-house at Inada.

Zensho-bo became the leader at Inada, and believers gathered around him, forming a group. Those who disagreed with Zensho-bo's views formed other groups. Difficulties arose among them, and weakened the unity and popularity of the Inada followers.

At Takada, a group was formed around Shinbutsu-bo of Senjuji.

People's attitutde toward Eshinni and her children gradually changed as the days went by. Eshinni, who was now no better than an ordinary widow, was gradually forgotten, and her life grew more and more difficult.

Zenran grew up under these circumstances. Iyanyo began to work in the household of Hino Hirotsuna in Kyoto.

As he grew up, Zenran was able to grasp the entire situation. He became a sturdy, adventurous young man. He began to feel that his nature conflicted with the Jodo Shinshu atmosphere around him.

The Nembutsu believers at Inada all seemed to him womanish, passive, and half-hearted. Their attitude was tantalizing.

Above all, he was deeply offended by Zensho-bo and others, who had taken over the meeting house of Inada, and were behaving in a lordly manner. He realized his own power and wanted to do something important in the Kanto Buddhist world.

He could not feel whole-hearted admiration for his father, being quite different. Thinking that his father was lacking in affection, Zenran even began to harbor a feeling of revolt.

He was sturdy and rough mannered, and possessed the power to awe others into obedience. He influenced people around him, although not deliberately. He called himself by the Buddhist name of Jishin-bo.

To the orthodox group at Inada led by Zensho-bo, Zenran's influence was a threat. Besides, he was capable of political strategy.

He influenced a man to say: " The meeting house at Inada was, in the first place, founded by Shinran Shonin, Jishin-bo's father. When the Shonin started on a pilgrimage, Jishin-bo was still young, and so the meeting house was temporarily put in Zensho-bo's charge. Jishin-bo has attained manhood now; therefore it is proper that he should succeed his father and become the leader."

Zensho-bo's group did not agree to this.

" There is no such thing as succession by family in regard to a meeting house," they said. " We saw the Shonin transfer the responsibility to Zensho Shonin with our own eyes, and there is not a bit of doubt about it. The rightful leader of the Inada group is Zensho Shonin."

Then Zenran's group circulated a rumor: " Jishin-bo has been chosen for the position of private secretary by

Shinran Shonin. Aimin-bo brought the meassage from the capital.''

Many of the followers in Hitachi and Shimotsuke provinces believed this rumor.

Zenran, being bold, was dissatisfied with the believers of the Easy Path of the ' Other Oower,' whom he considered weak and without practical ability. So he adopted some of the " self-effort " principles into his faith. Moreover, in order to attract untaught people to his side, he took advantage of their ignorance and introduced magic rites.

He was able to do these things because the power of the Nembutsu Sect of Inada had declined.

The orthodox group attacked Zenran's practices, saying magic was heresy, not the way of Jodo Shinshu.

Zenran's group then claimed that he had received this doctrine secretly from his father, the Shonin.

This threw the Kanto followers into utter confusion. Shinshu followers did not know what to do.

Jishin-bo was very popular, and many people believed what he said.

Zensho-bo's orthodox group sent a messenger to the Shonin, and asked whether Zenran's claims were true. Shinran was greatly troubled, and replied as follows:

" I have received your letter. It certainly is strange to hear that a person named Aimin-bo says he received a letter from me. I have never met him, nor written to him. So this is shocking to hear.

"And as for Jishin-bo's doctrine, I know nothing about

it.   You say that Jishin-bo told you that I taught him a
secret doctrine one night ; and that as a result, the followers in Hitachi and Shimotsuke are saying that I told
lies.

   " From now on, therefore, we are no longer father and
son."

Shinran tried to advise and teach Zenran, but the
latter refused to change, partly because of his revolt
against his father.

To make matters worse, Zenran started a lawsuit at
Rokuhara and Kamakura, exposing the internal dis-
agreements.

Shinran, who had a strong sense of justice, naturally
felt obligated to Zensho-bo and others who belonged
to the orthodox group.   Of course he could not defend
his son in any way.

Finally he disowned Zenran in a severe letter of renun-
ciation which said in part:

   " . . . Moreover, you have misled the Nembutsu
followers of Hitachi and Shimotsuke in the vital problem
of rebirth into the Pure Land, and have told lies about
your father—this is outrageous.   I hear you told them
that the Eighteenth Vow of Amida was as useless as a
withering flower.   You have committed the grave sin
of disparaging the Dharma.   This is extremely despica-
ble conduct.   From now on I am no longer your father,
nor are you my son."

This was done to defend the Dharma, and above all,

to do justice to the Kanto followers.

Shinran did not hate Zenran. He knew, better than anyone else, the Karma effects of individuals. Especially in his later years, he was deeply aware of this, and wept over his own Karma, while at the same time appreciating the great compassion of Amida.

Shinran must have seen Zenran's Karma effects in Zenran's own personal nature. Shinran knew that he himself bore the most responsibility for Zenran's birth, upbringing, and circumstances. He was too introspective to remain indifferent to Zenran's faults.

In a sense, Zenran's troubles were partly due to Shinran's Karma.

Above all, Shinran could not help realizing his responsibility for Zenran's antagonism. He asked himself whether he had brought up his son with love, and whether he had tried to prevent his son's weaknesses.

It would not be farfetched if he were criticized for being an irresponsible and indifferent father.

However, he also knew that this was an inevitable consequence of his duty, position, and discipline as a priest.

Then, was it right for a priest to marry and have children? Why hadn't he become a laymen, reciting the Nembutsu, and bringing up the children with affection, like ordinary fathers?

However hard Shinran thought about it, it was impossible for him to blame, scold and disown Zenran without a sense of guilt.

On the other hand, when he thought of the Shinshu

believers and the conditions they faced, Shinran's keen sense of honor forced him to take action and to disown Zenran.

When one's child quarrels with someone else's, the proper parent will scold his own child, out of consideration for the other child's parents, regardless of who is wrong.

Shinran could not help disowning Zenran, though this may seem inconsistent. Shinran's character is clearly illustrated here, and we cannot help sympathizing with him.

Zenran, though ambitious, was not wicked by nature, nor unworthy of his father. He had enough ability to start a religious movement. Therefore, people gathered around him. He inherited some of his father's nature, after all.

Time glides by. Eventually it buries everything. Anger and ill-feelings fade away with the passing of the years.

Years afterwards, Zenran came to the capital to live there for some time. One day he called at his father's cottage at Nishi-no-toin.

Zenran remembered his childhood, his father's farewell to Inada. His father had looked back for a second from the bridge, inclining his hat, and then had walked across and away.

But now he looked at his father and found, to his surprise, an old priest, bent, white browed, and wrinkled. His ill-feeling and anger toward his father disappeared immediately. There was only a feeling of pity for a fellow being subject to age and change.

"I am delighted to be able to visit you. I feared I might not be able to do this," Zenran said.

Shinran raised his eyes and looked intently at Zenran.

"Did you understand the meaning of Karma effects?"

"As I grew older I began to understand a little about the deeper meanings of things."

Shinran nodded.

"Matters concerning you and me are all the effects of our Karma. All hatred and ill-feelings are due to man's stupidity."

"I, Zenran, am unworthy of you. Please pardon me for causing you anxiety."

"Amida is the one who forgives, but I will, if you wish. Will you then forgive this merciless father?"

"Your words overwhelm me. Please feel at ease."

"Then please listen to what I say. In the first place, it is contradictory for a priest to marry. The resulting harm can be seen in you. Then one may ask why I married. My marriage was a deliberate means to spread the Buddhist teachings in the latter days of the Dharma, when discipline has declined, as the Buddha said it would. Most layman believers cannot recite the Nembutsu without marrying and having a family life. Therefore, Honen Shonin said: 'Those who can recite the Nembutsu by marrying should do so.'

"I married as a means of spreading the teachings, and thus I sacrificed myself for all. And the one who shared the greatest part of that sacrifice was you. So

I pity you, Jishin-bo. From birth you were fated never to receive your father's affection. Due to this Karma effect, you had to see the lonely life of your mother, who lived like a widow."

Zenran's head slowly drooped.

" Take pity on me, too. I had to marry in order to recite the Nembutsu; but I had to be alone in order to recite the Nembutsu. I was trapped in this contradictory situation. I had to marry in order to preach, but had to live alone for my religious devotion, due to my Karma. You have inherited this Karma from me. Don't you think ill-feelings and hatred are merely matters of minor importance? "

" What you said, Shonin, strikes deep into my heart. It was my shallow mind that made me bitter, and my ignorance of our Karma relationship."

" It is all the result of your Karma effect that you felt bitter toward me, showed signs of greediness, and started a wrong doctrine. The only thing you can do is to leave everything as it is and recite the Nembutsu."

" I do not know why, but I am proud and greedy by nature, and am unable to suppress these tendencies," said Zenran, deeply impressed.

" Consequently, I disturbed the Kanto followers by expressing heretical views, and started a lawsuit. I did not give in, though you disowned me. And until today I have never once inquired after your health. But now that I see your gentle countenance, I understand my nature so much better."

" Man's nature is all destined from previous

existences," said Shinran, evidently feeling compassion for his son. " I lacked energy by nature, and was always suppressed by others. The more I strived to be bold, the more I had to submit. And it was a burden all my life to mingle with people. It was for this reason that I left Inada.

" I have devoted myself to preaching for thirty years, against my nature, and so I am now spending the rest of my life all by myself, because that is my wish."

" It is enlightening to hear of your profound feelings," said Zenran. " As for me, I will recite the Nembutsu in accordance with my nature. How fortunate I am today—the doubt I have suffered for so long has melted away."

" I also feel a brightness like a spring day."

The old father and his son rejoiced, taking each other's hand.

Kenchi-bo, who had come from Takada and had been staying with Shinran then, suddenly opened the screen and came into the room without warning.

The father and son suddenly separated.

Kenchi-bo looked as if he knew nothing, but in his heart he was very glad to see the two reconciled.

Zenran went back to his home, and went on living in accordance with his nature, prospering as a religious leader.

Thirty years after Shinran's death, when Kakunyo Shonin passed through Murata in the province of Hitachi on his way to Kanto, he saw two or three hundred men and women, priests and nuns in hangings[1]

parading on horseback toward Kashima, crying:
" The Lord is going down to the beach.! "
This was Zenran's parade.

[1] *Mushi* or veil-like cloth hanging all around from the brim of a large brimmed hat. In olden times women wore this when they went out. This was a procession of Zenran and his followers. (It was put in probably to show that Zenran, unlike his father, still loved gorgeousness surrounded by followers.)

Chapter 29

WEEP FOR YOUR OWN KARMA

Iyanyo was a beautiful, unaffected girl, so she was popular since childhood. The Inada followers called her "Youngest Princess."

When she went to the temple, holding her mother's hand, she was a pretty sight.

She liked to gaze at the picture painted above the lintel in the temple, showing the heavenly maidens in fluttering, thin silk garments—some playing on the flute and some beating drums.

The girl was fond of wearing her holiday clothes of thin silk, like the maiden's in the picture. She knew no worldly cares.

She played with her naughty brother Zenran and other boys. She was strong-willed and clever for her age, and this made her more charming.

But with the sudden departure of her father from Inada, her circumstances changed completely—her mother became a nun; her brother became grouchy; her family was gradually forgotten by the people; and their income dwindled away.

Iyanyo did not like to be poor; she liked beautiful and interesting things.

She loved her mother and brother, but hated their gloomy life at Inada, because her life had previously been so carefree and comfortable.

In the village there lived a hemp merchant who went to the capital every year. He had been asked by the wife of Lord Hino Hirotsuna, one of his customers, to find her a maid.

He thought Iyanyo would be a good choice.

" Wouldn't you like to go to the capital? There's always something happening there. Besides, you may get a chance to see your father," he said.

" Oh, I would love to go there," she said yearningly. " But I know no one there who can help me."

" I know a good place for you. It is a court noble's household, and the lady is very kind."

" I would like to go. But I wonder if mother will allow me."

From that day Iyanyo began to beg her mother to send her to the capital. The hemp merchant added his arguments.

At first the mother disapproved, but gradually she gave in.

" Her nature is not suitable for the country life," the mother thought. " Besides, I would not like to make her a nun. I might as well send her to the capital."

Seeing that the mother was nearly persuaded, the merchant urged, " The girl is very eager to go. Moreover, she may have a chance to see her father,"

" But are you sure it is a reliable household? "

" A very well-mannered family. She can learn the manners of the capital, too."

The mother considered Iyanyo's nature, the country atmosphere which was getting more and moe unpleasant, and their financial problems, and finally decided to send her daughter to the capital.

The fifteen-year-old girl put on her best clothes and was taken to the capital by the hemp merchant.

The Hino family lived in Hanazono.

Hino Hirotsuna was young. His beautiful gentle wife was delicate and seldom healthy. She liked Iyanyo, who was always near to look after her.

In the autumn of the following year, the lady became ill and could hardly leave her bed. Iyanyo gave her the utmost care.

Soon that year came to an end, and a new spring came. But the lady did not get well.

Hirotsuna, a samurai of high character, remained true to his invalid wife.

Seventeen-year-old Iyanyo, lively, active and gay, attracted his attention. He did not make any advances, but his wife knew how he felt.

One hazy moonlit night in the spring, she spoke to her husband as he sat wearily by her bedside.

" You must be suffering because I am so ill."

" I am lonely, but that cannot be helped."

" What do you think of Iyanyo? "

" I think she is a lovely, diligent maid." He blushed.

" I was just wondering if she could serve you."

" Don't joke; "

" I am not joking. I'm so sorry for you and the consequences of my long illness. She is good-natured, naive and young, like the first blooming of a flower. She would be a far better choice than any stranger."

" It is cruel to pluck such a flower."

" To pluck it out of lust is cruel, but I consider her a sister, and we two could serve you. There are many such cases among the nobles."

" Though you say so, it would break your heart."

" No, I will not be jealous. Please be thinking about it," she asked earnestly.

" Though she looks like an adult, Iyanyo is still a child," he said.

After this conversation, Hirotsuna's affection for Iyanyo developed into sincere love.

In the autumn of that year, when they went to Arashi-yama to see the scarlet leaves, Hirotsuna stopped his carriage and walked among the trees with Iyanyo.

" You are as lovely as the reddening maple leaves," he told her.

" You are noble and handsome."

" Can you stay long with us? "

" I'm willing to serve you as long as you and your lady don't dismiss me."

" How can we dismiss you? It would be like losing a precious stone if you left us."

" I am so fortunate to serve a good family and ride in a carriage with a kind lord . . ." she was going to say, but she stopped, as if her conscience troubled her.

Instead she said, " Her ladyship is always confined to her room; you must be lonely."

" She tells me that she considers you as her sister, and so . . ."

" And so what did she say? " asked Iyanyo, her heart fluttering.

" She told me to care for you," he said hurriedly, and looked at her with piercing eyes.

She blushed and covered her face with her flowing sleeve.

After that Iyanyo's attitude toward him changed.

The lady called Iyanyo to her bedside one quiet evening, when the deer were calling in the woods.

She said sincerely, " I think of you as my younger sister, so I wish you would think of me as your elder sister."

" That is more than I deserve.   I have been so thankful for all your kindness since the first day I met you."

" I don't know why, but I like you.   As I am an invalid, I feel so sorry for my lord.   Since I consider you my sister, won't you serve him in my place? "

Iyanyo did not answer.   Her head dropped.

" Since you do not answer—I suppose you don't like the idea? "

" I cannot be his mistress.   I am a daughter of a priest."

" By no means a mistress, my sister.   You would be the second consort.   In ancient T'ang China, Huayang was Yang Kuei Fei's sister, but they both became wives of Emperor Huan Tsung.   Moreover, the lord is not a lustful person. He loves you from the bottom of his heart."

Iyanyo only dropped her head lower.

The lady then said, " How stupid of me! A girl like you can't make such a decision right away. Please be thinking about it."

This matter began to torment Iyanyo. It was even painful for her to look at Hirotsuna.

Hirotsuna looked at her with burning eyes. But he never acted in an indecent manner.

A new year came and she became eighteen years old.

The cherry blossoms looked languishing. Hirotsuna could no longer remain silent.

On their way back from a flower-viewing excursion, he took her hand in his.

" How long are you going to keep me waiting? "

Iyanyo did not answer.

He released her hand.

" I'd better give up. You do not love me."

" My lord, I have a father who lives in this city. He is a teacher-priest living in seclusion at Nishi-no-toin. I wonder what he'll say. I'm sure he will not allow me to serve a lord who has a wife."

" I am not after pleasure," he said. " I am truly in love with you."

" I know it well."

" My wife's wishes are different from those of or- dinary people. She does not mean to put you to shame."

' But I shouldn't do it without my father's

permission."

She was greatly worried. Such an intimate matter could not be explained easily. She wondered whether her father would approve.

Full of anxiety, she went to Nishi-no-toin to see her father. But she was unable to discuss the matter with him, and came back more downhearted than ever.

"What did your father say?" Hirotsuna asked anxiously.

"I came home without telling him about it."

"Iyanyo, I will never let you go." He took her hands tightly in his. "You are mine, no matter what anyone might say."

She was trembling.

Hirotsuna put his mouth to her ear and said, "Do you love me?"

"Yes."

He embraced her.

"What if father doesn't approve. . . ." She sobbed suddenly, putting her face against his chest. "I cannot leave you."

Thus was begun Iyanyo's life of love.

People thought she was only Hirotsuna's mistress, and this gossip troubled her father and mother. It is always the way of the world to draw the wrong conclusion and not try to learn the truth.

Above all, the lady's relatives thought the affair improper. They did not try to understand her motives, or to sympathize with Iyanyo.

Iyanyo was happy only with Hirotsuna, for the rest

of the world regarded her heartlessly.

Months and years went by.

Hirotsuna, who had been in good health, suddenly became very ill and soon died.

Iyanyo was like a fish out of water.

But she consoled her sickly mistress and looked after the household, whose fortunes declined rapidly after the death of the master.

It was practically the same fate suffered by her own family in Inada.

The Hino relatives began planning to throw her out. She was no longer needed.

The lady objected to these plans but being ill and dependent on her parents' family, she could do nothing except to worry.

Iyanyo became tired of the relatives' persistent demands and hated to cause her lady anxiety. The proud, honorable young woman finally decided to leave the Hino family, without even asking for anything.

The lady wept at their parting.

" If I had known what was going to happen, I wouldn't have asked you to serve Hirotsuna. I don't have the words to apologize for causing you so much suffering."

" It was a fate no one could have predicted."

" Do you have a place to stay? "

" No, I have no particular place in mind."

" I hear Lord Kuga Michimitsu is looking for someone to serve in his family. Shall I write a letter for you? "

" I don't want to serve in a noble family again.

Since the death of the lord, I feel like a nun at heart. If you know of any lady who is a devout Buddhist, please introduce me to such a person."

The lady thought for a while and said, " I know of a good person by the name of Sho-amidabutsu, who was once a court-lady. She is a nun now and lives a lonely life in Higashiyama. I will write to her about you."

Thus Iyanyo, who had just become twenty, called at Sho-amidabutsu's dwelling, heavy-hearted after her stormy tragedy.

At Matsubara, Higashiyama, the nun lived a quiet life which was unlike that of a nun or a lay woman.

When Iyanyo called, the nun was cleaning her altar.

She was an elegant-looking woman just past fifty years of age.

After reading Lady Hino's letter, she said to Iyanyo with kind eyes, " Life here is not easy, but if you don't mind the hardship, please stay and help me."

" Thank you very much."

Iyanyo could not help thinking that the nun looked like her mother Eshinni.

The girl thought of how her feelings had changed, compared with the time she first had come to the capital. She hadn't cared for the life of a nun before, but now she appreciated it more than a life with a noble family.

Sho-amidabutsu, too, after losing her husband, had probably suffered other distressing experiences, for she often told Iyanyo how unreliable worldly things were.

" A Sutra says: ' The world is like the dew and the

lightning,' " said the nun. " My past life illustrates
this. Man's life is as fleeting as the dew, but I had
counted upon the flashing happiness of the lightning."

Iyanyo was deeply impressed by these words.

" Even now it is just the same," continued the nun.
" I don't know how long this present life will last. But
what is different is that now I know it is only temporary;
I do not rely on it."

" I think I can understand," said Iyanyo modestly.
Being young, she felt she should not act as if she knew
a lot about life.

" There is nothing that can be relied upon in this
world. I only trust in the Buddha," said the nun.

Iyanyo spent the days with the nun, copying Sutras
and visiting sacred places in and near the capital.

Sho-amidabutsu, being timid by nature, was afraid of
the world, and did not know how to economize. She
was one who could not get along without a patron, but
she didn't want one.

The woman had spent her savings over the years. She
did not want to beg as the mendicant nuns did.

" I hear your father is a priest. Where does he
live? " asked the nun.

" He lives at Gojo Nishi-no-toin."

" To what sect does he belong? "

" To a sect called Jodo Shinshu."

" I have never heard of it."

" It is a new sect my father established in Kanto."

" What? He established a new sect? And what is
your father's name? "

" Now he calls himself Gutoku Shinran. Formerly he was called Zenshin-bo, and was a disciple of Honen Shonin."

The nun was surprised.

" Then isn't he the Zenshin-bo who was involved in the religious disturbance of the Shogen Era and was exiled to Echigo? "

" Yes, I hear that happened forty years ago."

" Well, why didn't you tell me about it? "

" People have forgotten all about it, and I thought it was pointless to talk about it."

" Yes, the people of the capital have forgotten, but I still remember it clearly. I was young then, and I often visited Yoshimizu with my husband. Though I had not met the Reverend Zenshin-bo, my faith in the Nembutsu was established then."

The nun seemed to be overwhelmed with recollections of the old days.

" How glad I am to hear that Zenshin-bo is now in the capital. I certainly would like to meet him. Will you please take me to Nishi-no-toin? "

" That can be done easily."

On the following evening, the two walked in the moonlight and visited Shinran's dwelling in Nishi-no-toin.

Shinran had been sitting on the veranda, gazing blankly at the moonlit sky and meditating.

" This is Sho-amidabutsu," said Iyanyo, introducing the nun to her father.

Shinran said, " Thank you for your kindness to my

daughter."

The nun replied, " By some ties from previous existences, I have been living under the same roof with your daughter. But I did not know her father was Shonin until she told me last night. I was very surprised."

" People have forgotten me now. It is nice of you to remember."

" I still recall the religious disturbance of the Shogen Era. My husband and I were converted to the Nembutsu faith at about that time. We heard that you were exiled to Echigo, but after that nothing was heard about you. My husband died after that, and now I spend my days reciting the Nembutsu."

" Oh, is that so? It was forty years ago."

He was silent for some time.

" The world has changed, and the people have, too," said Shinran quietly. " But what is unchangeable is the Nembutsu."

" Yes, indeed. With the passing of the years, it is the Nembutsu that becomes more and more dependable. Nothing else is reliable."

" It was well said: ' Everything is false and silly— there is nothing true.' "

Sho-amidabutsu, who had been looking around her, said, " Considering your advanced age, you should have more than the barest necessities of life. Have you any motive in living thus? "

The Shonin smiled and replied, " No, I am living thus because I cannot help it; not because I prefer it."

The nun did not seem to understand.

" Isn't it a priest's preference to live a lonely life, not heeding the flowers? "

" I once had such esthetic desires long ago, but I have given up such a pretense."

" Is it pretense? "

" Yes. That is because one is not truly poor; there are further extremes possible. At present I would like to live in a better-looking hut, and would like to have at least an acolyte. But I cannot afford it—this is what we call poverty. To wish to remain in loneliness— this is a sort of esthetic pleasure. At present I have no time for such things."

" If so, wouldn't a person be enslaved by poverty, and always filled with discontent? "

" That is the reality of poverty. But to live in this reality—enduring poverty, the effects of one's Karma, and feeling grateful for Amida's great desire to save mankind—this should be the true life of the Nembutsu."

Sho-amidabutsu was greatly moved.

" I understand now for the first time. I thought the Nembutsu followers should lead blameless lives. But as my savings gradually were spent, I had to demand the payment of a loan made a long time ago, and had to argue down the prices of the things I bought. I have been ashamed of such contradictions. But now I understand that the recitation of the Nembutsu along with these sufferings should be our life of thanks for Amida's great mercy."

Shinran nodded approval and said, " You will have

to suffer more from now on. Your present life is an escape from the suffering world. But in the future you may have to go out into that world, stripped of everything. Then you will recall what I have said."

"What a true illustration of the life of Nembutsu you have shown me! I am deeply impressed. This brief meeting has proved to be a profound experience for me. Will you please let me call on you from time to time?"

"You may come at any time. Abandon all thoughts of formality and speak truly and frankly."

The nun, deeply impressed by Shinran's words, left Nishi-no-toin with Iyanyo.

They were walking toward Gojo Bridge when she said, "The Shonin is a great teacher. Indeed, the recitation of the Nembutsu should be as he described."

Iyanyo, too, said thoughtfully, "I am ashamed of my unworthiness, when my father is such a teacher."

When they reached the bridge, they saw a court-lady in a palanquin.

"Reverend Sho-amidabutsu."

"Oh, Lady Hingashi. Where are you going?"

"I hear there is a rare performance of court dances and music by Shirabyoshi[3] dancers at Nijo Kiyamachi, so I am hurrying to see it. I hope you will come and see me at my home in Karasumaru."

"Come and see me, too, at Higashiyama."

"Certainly I will, in a few days. Good-bye."

[1] White-robbed women dancers of late Heian and Kamakura periods who wore noblemen's headgears and swords.

Lady Hingashi's palanquin hurried down the avenue.

" Who was she, may I ask? " said Iyanyo.

" There are all sorts of people in the world.   She is a distant relative of my late husband.   I taught her to play the koto when she was young.   Now she is the concubine of a court official, and frequently attends events such as Sarugaku plays and Shirabyoshi dances. She has a sweet disposition, and although her life is the exact opposite of mine, we have always been good friends."

The two returned to their home in Matsubara, talking of worldly affairs.

Chapter 30

A WOMAN TRANSFERRING HER BONDAGE

After she met Shinran, a different light began to shine on Sho-amidabutsu's spiritual life. She began to open her eyes to the real world.

She learned to recite the Nembutsu, which she had disregarded heretofore, because she thought it lacked beauty and significance. But now she was eager to appreciate the great mercy of Amida, by facing reality in her daily sorrow and happiness.

Her esthetic desire to live a lonely life decreased after hearing Shinran's strict explanation.

Strangely, she began to see the good side of the world. The countless people who crowded the dusty streets began to look friendly to her. Her superior attitude and contempt toward the world had greatly diminished.

On the other hand, her life became more and more difficult. Her savings were nearly gone. In order to make a living, she would have to beg for alms, seek employment, or go into business.

One evening when Iyanyo removed the offering of rice

from the altar and threw it in the yard, the sparrows came down from the roofs to eat it, as they always did.

Sho-amidabutsu saw this and thought, " The sparrows, too, are eating what is given to them—there is always somebody who takes pity on them."

She then called Iyanyo, and said hesitantly, " I would like you to leave my service."

" For what reason? " Iyanyo was surprised. " Did I do something that hurt your feelings? "

" Not at all. I am indebted to you for your kind help. I can't tell you how relieved I have been since you came. Above all, I have received spiritual comfort, because you introduced me to the Shonin. If I could have it my way, I would want you to continue to stay with me, but to tell the truth . . ."

She blushed and continued, " My savings are all gone, and now I must seek a livelihood. I cannot afford a companion, so I am forced to ask you to leave."

Iyanyo made a quick decision.

" All right, I will. If that is the reason, I will take my leave. I must thank you for looking after a person as unmannered as I."

The nun was moved to tears.

" Poverty is a terrible thing. If I were as well-to-do as I used to be, I would have you stay with me without doing anything, no matter how many years. But now I must ask you to leave me. The situation is beyond my control, and I am helpless."

" Please do not worry. I know your situation well. I am not concerned, because I have been making my

own living since I was fifteen.   I will be greatly obligated
if you will let me stay until I find a place to go."

" Of course.   I will be doing all the cooking and
washing and everything by myself.   It turned out
exactly as the Shonin said : ' I am not doing this because
I like it ; I cannot help it.' "

Iyanyo looked for a place to live, but could not find
any.

A letter came from her mother Eshinni, who had
not written for a long time.   It said :

> " Last year most of the crops were very poor, and the
> people are miserable.   They feel they cannot make a
> living here, and some have moved away.   Several of our
> relatives who were helping us have lost their means of
> livelihood.   Since most people are in difficulty, we have
> no one to rely on.
>
> " Two men who had been in our service died in
> January, so there is no one to cultivate our fields.   But as
> it is useless to worry about worldly affairs, I consider
> them to be effects of my Karma and simply recite the
> Nembutsu.   Really, there is little we can rely on in this
> world.
>
> " I am so glad you sent me a kimono.   You must have
> grown, and how I miss you !   Be sure to recite the Nem-
> butsu so you can attain rebirth into the Pure Land,
> where everything will be bright."

Iyanyo finished reading the letter and thought of her
lonely mother-nun in far-off Kanto.

Sho-amidabutsu returned from a visit.

" Have you found a place to go ? she asked the girl.

" I'm sorry, I have not found a place yet."

" Then how about the home of Lady Hingashi, whom we met at Gojo Bridge some days ago? Today I called on her at Karasumaru and asked whether she could employ you, and she consented."

" It must be a prosperous household. I wonder whether I can be useful there."

"Do not worry. You will be confident when you meet her—she is such a good, sincere person. I'm sure you will find her congenial."

" Then I will be glad to go there," said Iyanyo, who could afford no delay.

Lady Hingashi's household staff agreed formally to Iyanyo's employment.

The nun showed a document to Iyanyo, as if she did not know what to do with it.

" Lady Hingashi is childishly ignorant of worldly matters, so an attendant looks after her affairs. This attendant asked for a written agreement in accordance with the service law."

Iyanyo looked at the document and felt miserable, but pretended she did not feel anything.

" One should expect something like this, if she is employed in another's household," she said.

The nun looked away and said, " This is the cruel attendant's fault. Lady Hingashi could not have done it. Please don't feel badly."

Iyanyo called on her father at Nishi-no-toin the following day, and told him everything, showing him the agreement.

Shinran looked at his daughter and examined the document. " Namu-Amida-Butsu," he recited, without showing any emotion, his eyes clear and serene.

He then took his brush and quickly wrote the following:

Transferring Iyanyo's Employment

This maid is in the service of Sho-amidabutsu, but has been assigned by the latter to serve Lady Hingashi. There is no one who objects or will interfere with this. I hereby certify this for future reference.

Yours truly,
Shinran

The father and daughter knew each other's mind. Iyanyo knew her father cared. If he did not believe in the Nembutsu, he would have wept bitterly, embracing her. Though young, Iyanyo could understand how his painful grief was transformed into the serene utterance of the Nembutsu.

Shinran did not try to explain, or to make a long apology for his helplessness. Words were useless. Iyanyo was a martyr due to the effects of her Karma. What she could do was to appreciate the great mercy of Amida.

Fortunately, Lady Hingashi was a good person, as Sho-amidabutsu had said. Iyanyo had never seen such a frank, honest person whose feelings were never guarded, and Iyanyo liked her from their first meeting. She had been just like the lady when she was young and ignorant of the hardships of life. She found she could behave naturally in the lady's presence, without any need to be cautious. The lady was willful and full of faults, but even a devil would not hate her. Iyanyo felt she had arrived at the carefree world which she had imagined before coming to the capital.

" I wish to be taken into your service starting today."

She put her hands down in obeisance.

The lady greeted her and said, " Certainly. I am not a cheerless person like the Reverend Sho-amida-butsu. Please remember that I am an unmannered court lady."

Lady Hingashi liked Iyanyo very much, and chose her to be her personal maid. There were many others who could have been chosen, and who might have been jealous of Iyanyo, but she was not mistreated, thanks to the lady's protection.

The lady took Iyanyo with her whenever she went any-where.

She was fond of going about the capital attending various performances. On such occasions she somehow attracted people's attention, although she had no desire to do so.

Three or four days after Iyanyo came to serve in the household, the lord visited the lady. He was still young. What impressed Iyanyo was that the lady loved him from the bottom of her heart. Usually so willful, she was completely faithful to the lord and seemed to care more than he did. This, too, gave Iyanyo a good impression.

During the noble lord's visit, koto and flutes were

played. The lady always looked forward to the lord's visits. When he was in a low mood, she worried like a child.

She told Iyanyo about her love affairs. The latter listened, holding back her laughter.

The lady began to be very particular about Iyanyo's dresses and make-up, because the maid was her constant attendant and companion when she went anywhere.

One day when Iyanyo visited Sho-amidabutsu to greet and thank her, the latter came out of the kitchen, wiping her hands.

" Oh, how beautiful you have become! And you look far more cheerful than while you were here."

" My lady is very particular about me."

" How do you like your duties? "

" They are just splendid."

" I'm very glad to hear that."

" How are you getting along here? "

" I have become somewhat accustomed to living alone, but I am not satisfied with this life. Now I want to come in contact with the real world."

" I understand your feeling."

" I am thinking about it now. One of these days I would like to call on the Shonin and talk with him."

" I will come again soon. I just dropped in to thank you."

While Iyanyo was away, a visitor had arrived. People were talking gaily in the lady's room.

The visitor was a painter called Onomiya Zennen. The lady introduced Iyanyo to him as her relative.

" She was in a temple recently and was about to become a nun," the lady said. " I thought she was too beautiful to become a nun, and so I brought her here."

Zennen laughed.

All kinds of people visited the lady—samurai, traders, diviners, poets, court dancers, Shirabyoshi dancers, nuns. The lady selected friends fastidiously from all walks of life.

Iyanyo's life was free and full of variety. Her personality blossomed.

" Your father is a great priest, I hear," said the lady.

" He is living in seclusion now."

" I am afraid of a great priest—I feel he would see through my heart. A nun is my preference. Let's go and see Sho-amidabutsu. I have not been there for some time, although I promised to go."

Accompanied by Iyanyo, she rode in a palanquin to Higashiyama Matsubara.

" Oh, how nice of you to come and see me," the nun greeted them.

" I haven't been here for some time. It is a pleasant place."

There came soft sounds of water dripping from the bamboo pipe, and the warbling of a nightingale.

" You may be interested to know that I am not satisfied with my life," said the nun.

" How strange! I did not expect to hear such a thing from you."

" I have begun to feel that I would like to come in contact with the world a little."

" I don't want you to be anything except a nun."

" I would like something a nun could do."

The three thought for some time.

" Besides, I have no abilities that could earn me a living," said the nun.

" I wonder what business a nun could operate," said Lady Hingashi.

" How about selling pottery? I know how to make clay vessels such as rice bowls, flower vases and wine jugs. I will make dolls, too. Moreover, dyed goods should be profitable. I will display these articles in a shop, which will combine the features of a hermitage, a shop, and a tea pavilion. And I will appear in the shop in nun's attire, What do you think about this idea? "

" I think it would be interesting," said Lady Hingashi, tapping her knee. " You know how to compose poems and draw pictures, so pictures and poems on the clay vessels would be excellent."

" It sounds interesting," said Iyanyo.

" But I need funds."

" You need not worry about the small amount you will need," said Lady Hingashi, who was willing to take the responsibility.

" You had better begin right away," said she, impulsive as usual.

" I'm so glad you will help me. I must talk to the Shonin about this, and get started as soon as possible."

" There is a painter called Onomiya Zennen, who comes to my house often. He has many other talents, so you can consult him about construction, the location of the kiln, and dyed goods."

"That would be excellent. Please, will you speak to him about it?"

The lady said, after more thought, "Your idea is very interesting, but I hope you will not be dragged completely into worldly matters. I hope you will not become too interested in business and forget your Buddhist duties."

Sho-amidabutsu smiled and said, "You need not worry about that. But what I fear is that the shop might 'run away' from me."

"Yes, that's right. You are best as a nun. You were born with a pure heart. If you give up your hermitage, I will not have a place to go when my lord forsakes me, you know," Lady Hingashi laughed.

"Don't joke."

"It's not a joke. I am going to be a nun when I am forsaken."

"Don't say such an unlucky thing," said Iyanyo worriedly.

"My goodness, she wants to talk about her love affairs even when she comes here. Remember, I am single," the nun, and the three women laughed.

Lady Hingashi talked until dark and departed with Iyanyo.

Sho-amidabutsu felt excited as she thought of her new life. It might be a small matter to anyone else, but meant a great change in her life.

"Henceforth I am not going to escape from the world;

I am going to associate with it," she thought.

" This also is due to the inspiration I received from the Shonin. I will call on him and tell him about my resolution."

A few days later, the nun visited the Shonin, who had moved to Sanjo Tominokoji. She again found him in most uncomfortable circumstances.

" Shonin, I intend to open a shop," she said.

" A shop? I see." He looked at her face.

" I feel I should start having more to do with the world around me."

Shinran nodded approval.

" I want to live in the world and recite the Nembutsu, not get away from the world."

" That is what we should do."

" Besides, I cannot make a living otherwise."

Shinran remained silent.

" What you said has come true. My savings ran out, and I did everything I could, living without an attendant, but it wasn't enough. So I made up my mind to open a shop with the help of a friend."

" What kind of shop will it be? "

" A shop of earthenware. I have had experience in using a kiln, so I am going to make rice bowls, flower vases, and wine bottles. On these I will write poems and draw pictures. Besides, I intend to produce dolls and artistically dyed goods. I will display these in the tiny shop, which will be used as a tea room, too. The form of the hermitage will be retained, and I shall continue to wear nun's clothing. What do you think about it?"

"That will be interesting," said Shinran. "Your decision to do this is a step forward in your life, or rather, you have advanced closer to the great compassion of Amida. Nothing is easier than to avoid worldly matters, regarding them as unpleasant. But this is merely the easiest way. We cannot go on living unless we are able to associate with and exist in the unpleasant world. We call this 'man's mutual compassion.' There is selfishness in an unpleasant attitude. It is too simple to think that you alone are right. For there are delightful things in the world, too. It is delightful to encounter the good side of human nature. Even if it happens just once in ten times or once in a hundred times, you feel that men are all Buddha's children after all."

"As I am weak-hearted, I do not know if I can steer a successful course through the world; but I would like to carry out my plans."

"Go ahead and try—there is no alternative."

Sho-amidabutsu, deeply impressed, wrote the following poem and gave it to the Shonin:

> "Accepting the fate
> That I cannot escape,
> I tread this path
> Single-mindedly—
> May you help me!"

The Shonin nodded approval, and with eyes full of compassion, looked at the nun. Sho-amidabutsu thought that the Shonin knew everything.

Even if she were unsuccessful, she would not mind, she thought, for the Shonin had understood. Tears welled up in her eyes.

The Shonin, who escorted her to the garden gate, gently patted her shoulder and said, " Do not worry. They say there is no devil in one's walk through life."

Warmed by Shinran's deep affection, which was like a loving father's, the nun walked back to her home in Matsubara.

Chapter 31

THE OPENING OF THE SHOP

Encouraged by the Shonin, Sho-amidabutsu began preparing to open her shop.

Lady Hingashi, due to her temperament, wanted the nun to make a pretentious start, and said that she would furnish any funds necessary. But the nun decided to avoid extravagance, and emphasized the religious theme and elegance.

Onomiya Zennen helped her with the preparations.

A kiln was installed; the furnishings were completed; a tea pavilion was designed to harmonize with the landscaping and religious theme.

The shop's name, " Shoa-ken,"[1] was written on a signboard by the Shonin.

But it took time to make the clay vessels and dolls and dyed goods, so it was not until the vernal equinox of the following year that the shop was opened.

Matsubara, the shop's location, was a good one near Kiyomizu and Gion. In the shop, articles were neatly

[1] " Shoa " is taken from the nun's name, Sho-amidabutsu, but it literally means " to shine on a bower." " Ken " means a " house."

displayed; a willow and a cherry tree adorned the garden; and a light green rug was spread in the tea pavilion.

On the opening day Lady Hingashi sent various people to pose as purchasers, thus making the shop seem popular. The front was crowded, and many passers-by stopped to take a look. Sho-amidabutsu in nun's attire attracted much attention.

The shop had features that quickly appealed to people of refined taste.

There were some who rested in the tea pavilion, where the willow tree hung its leaves. The maids were all small girls in simple clothes, and they made a good impression.

A customer examined the merchandise and said, " This is a good shop. The articles are in excellent taste, and the prices are reasonable."

" Please call again when you come this way."

" I will mention this place to others," he promised, and bought a flower vase and a rice bowl.

Onomiya Zennen and Iyanyo were also present at the opening celebration.

" This is quite a success," said Zennen, smiling.

" Thanks to you all, the shop has made a fair start."

" At this rate, I'm sure you will have many customers," said Iyanyo and congratulated the nun.

" It would be nice to display square " shikishi " paper,[1] rectangular " tanzaku " paper,[2] and writing

---

[1] A piece of square paper for writing poems and painting pictures.

[2] A piece of long colored paper for writing poems.

paper with poems and drawings on them. But these would take time to produce, so I will ask some competent people to help you," said Zennen.

"That is a good idea. I would like to make changes gradually."

"You will soon be very busy. You will have to compose poems and bake bean-curd," said Zennen, laughing.

"It is better to be busy. It won't do if even a sparrow does not perch."[1]

"No. You'll soon see a lucky stork coming," Zennen said, laughing again.

But he became serious. "It would be troublesome if prosperity led you to build a large establishment. It is just right if you earn just enough to make a living. For you know, business can make a slave of you."

"That really is something we must realize," replied the nun, who felt that his words were a warning.

Just then Lady Hingashi came with her attendants and followers.

"It's nice to see everything going so well."

"Thanks to all you have done, the shop has made a good start."

"Today I have brought some customers. All of you, please make as many purchases as you can."

"Well, well," said the nun, smiling.

Each of the visitors bought one or two things and sat in the pavilion.

[1] "Even a sparrow does not perch" in an unpopular, deserted spot, according to a Japanese verse.

They drank the tea offered by the maids, and looked around them.

" What a pleasant place this is! I don't know why but I feel at rest," said one of them.

" It's only a single cherry tree, and yet I feel the thrill of flower-viewing! "

" This is really a fine way of making a living."

Sho-amidabutsu treated them to baked rice-curd and rice cakes, making the visitors happier.

They started on their way home, hoping that fortune would favor the admirable undertaking.

Chapter 32

TAKING A WIFE

The years went by.

Lady Hingashi had been downcast lately because the lord's visits had been few and far between. She thought his love had cooled, perhaps because he had found a new sweetheart.

The lady, who had been so fond of gorgeous affairs, quit attending performances of music and dances. She never went out, and hardly touched her meals.

The household had become as still as death, without music or laughter. Being in bad humor, she snarled at her maids, until they didn't know what to do.

She stopped receiving guests, saying it was wearisome, and opened her heart only to her distant relative, Onomiya Zennen, and her personal attendant, Iyanyo.

" The lord has become tired of me, for I have grown older," she said.

" That is your silly imagination," said Iyanyo.

" No, I'm right. It's natural, for my beauty is fading."

" The lord loves you sincerely. I know it. There

must be some reason."

" If so, he would have told me."

" There may be matters men cannot disclose."

" The lord and I fell in love ten years ago, before he became a lord. Men prosper more and more, but women's beauty gradually fades. This is my problem. How miserable it is to try to sustain a man's love that is cooling! But I love him. I cannot live if he forsakes me. I don't know why but I could not give him up even if it meant my death."

" If you love him so, your feelings will certainly be evident to his heart. Try to be calm and patient for a while," said Iyanyo.

" Why, you, too, are saying the same thing. If I could wait patiently, I would not be in such confusion. I am troubled and restless, wondering what I should do if he should forsake me. I am scared—I lay awake all night."

" You are worrying too much."

Lady Hingashi shook her head and said, " You cannot understand things like this. Please stop trying to comfort me." She was displeased.

Onomiya Zennen arrived just then, so Iyanyo felt relieved.

Zennen drew closer to the lady and said, " That you have such affection for him must be due to your ties from a previous existence. However, the lord does not have a lawful wife, and besides, he has duties at court, so occasionally he may not be able to visit you. I will find out what the matter is, so in the meantime, please eat regularly and live normally."

" Then will you please inquire quickly? I am dying to see him."

When Zennen looked into the matter, he found that there was trouble, as he had expected.

Those around the lord had been urging him to take a wife, and he could no longer refuse, for several reasons.

Zennen was surprised at the accuracy of the lady's premonition.

The lord said to Zennen, heaving a sigh, " Lady Hingashi and I have known each other for a long time, ever since the celebration of my coming of age. How can I forsake her now that she has grown older?

" Besides, she is as lovable as an infant. No matter who criticizes me, I don't have the courage to abandon her.

" However, I must consider the family lineage, relatives, and court duties, and I cannot get along without a wife. I have to make Lady Hingashi understand this, but when I think about how sad she would look, I don't have the heart to tell her. Consequently my visits have been few.

" Fortunately, you are her distant relative and she trusts you, so I would be most grateful if you would tell her my problems and make her understand."

Zennen thought this was an inevitable course of events.

He was the only person who could make the lady listen, so he explained the circumstances and told her she must resign herself to her fate.

As expected, she burst into tears and wept aloud.

" How miserable it is to grow older, and to be a commoner! My jewel of a lord will be taken away from me! "

She was thrown into despair, and said, " I will be pitied, not loved. I no longer possess the charms I had—the springtime of my life has passed! "

Those around her could do nothing except to wait until she stopped weeping.

Looking very melancholy, she finally said to Iyanyo, " I think it's more honorable to part from him than to be pitied, but I cannot do it. It's better to die than to part.

" Even if I were pitied, it would be better than being forsaken by him. What a miserable feeling it is! I know it well, but I cannot do otherwise."

The lady's distress touched Iyanyo's heart. How pitiful, she thought.

" I am not speaking words I do not mean. You say you are to be pitied, but I think you are being over-anxious. The lord loves you, and you are still beautiful. Please try to be cheerful."

But the lady remained sad, and never went any-where.

Late in autumn, crickets sang under the rocks in the garden. Seeing Lady Hingashi looking melancholy, Iyanyo said to her, " Shall we go to Makuzugahara?[1] We haven't been there for some time."

But the lady suddenly said, " Please take me to your

[1] Name of the district where Sho-amidabutsu lived.

father's place. I want to see him."

Iyanyo accompanied the lady to Shinran Shonin's lonely dwelling at Sanjo Tominokoji. He had already heard about the lady from Iyanyo. He knew she was naive and had the potential to appreciate Buddhism. He was sorry she had not had the chance to appreciate Amida's wonderful Vow to save mankind.

" Thank you very much for your kindess to Iyanyo," he said.

" It's I who is receiving the kindness, for I was born unusually dull in spiritual understanding."

" The Buddha extends his compassion to all who are in spiritual darkness."

" Moreover, I am suffering day and night, not knowing what to do about love and passion."

" It is the same with me," said Shinran. " I rise and fall in the ocean of passion and there is no escape. Though I am a priest, I had two wives. I have children, but am unable to look after their future. I am such a powerless sinner."

" How can we rid ourselves of this suffering of passion ? "

" There is nothing we can do but to suffer as we are."

" Then how can we be saved? "

" By enduring your sufferings—this is salvation."

" What is ' rebirth through the Nembutsu'? "

" Leave your sufferings as they are, realizing that you cannot get away from them, and call the name of the great, merciful Amida. This we call the ' rebirth through the Nembutsu.' "

Tears fell down the lady's cheeks.

" I did not know that Buddhism was like this. I had been letting the days pass, intoxicated by cherry blossoms and the moon. Lately I was overwhelmed by my troubles, and so I called on you and received this most unexpected teaching. I wonder whether it was devised purposely for me."

" You may well think so. When I ponder over the Eighteenth Vow of Amida, I sometimes think that it was created purposely for my sake."

" Then you feel the same? "

" Every man's feeling is the same—do not think suffering is yours alone. Everything in this world of ours changes—the beauty of flowers, a man's feelings. After ten years a change in a man's feelings is unavoidable. To watch with tranquility as love changes— isn't this what true love should be? We would like to stop what is changing. But to take life as it is and recite Amida's Name—this is what we call the life of the Nembutsu."

" Hearing the holy teachings, I feel as though the disorder of my mind has vanished. Please, will you continue to guide me? "

" You don't have to change your nature, or give up your feelings—leave everything as it is—just utter the Nembutsu as you live your life. The rest will take care of itself."

Lady Hingashi went home cheerfully.

After that she regained her will to live, and learned

how comforting it was to recite the Nembutsu. Things which had been neglected got on the right track again. She recovered her cheerfulness, too. She did not say disagreeable things to the lord. She was jealous at times, but only momentarily, and went on loving him and taking care of him as she had done before.

One day Sho-amidabutsu stood by the kiln of Shoa-ken, talking to Lady Hingashi. " You, too, have learned to recite the Nembutsu after all, haven't you?" she asked.

" Yes, after all. And you never told me of such a valuable teaching."

" Even if I had, you wouldn't have listened. Ha-ha-ha."

" Yes, time is a wonderful thing, isn't it? "

" It's like making porcelain—the heat gradually filling the kiln," said the nun.

" Well, you have become a regular merchant," the other smiled. " How changed you are! "

" I have changed since I received the Shonin's teaching."

" He is truly great."

" You and I were similar in temperament from our young days. But now we have really become fellow believers."

" That reminds me—Iyanyo and Mr. Onomiya would make a well-matched couple. What do you think about it? "

" I think so, too. You had better arrange the match."

Soon afterwards, Iyanyo and Zennen were united in marriage.

Chapter 33

NIRVANA[1]

In the autumn dusk, the fading sun shone on the garden of Zenbo-in at Matenokoji.

Shinran Shonin was having a friendly talk with his attendant and disciple, Yuien-bo, in a room where the paper sliding screens had been opened on the veranda.

" Shonin, the wings of the dragonfly have grown weak. There is one fluttering in the sun by the eaves, but it's going to die soon, isn't it? "

The Shonin peered at the fluttering dragonfly. " It's pitiful, isn't it? " he said.

They were silent for some time.

" Shonin," said Yuien-bo, coming nearer, " I have a problem which I would like to solve. I am assured of my rebirth into the Pure Land by reciting the Nembutsu. And I know that the Pure Land is a place where there is no suffering, but only comfort; whereas this world is full of suffering.

" But why is it that I do not wish to die so as to be

[1] The state of perfect peace, everlasting light and life, enlightenment—Buddhahood.

reborn into the Pure Land? I was ill last month, but I did not want to die then, no matter how unpleasant this world is. Will you please tell me why I feel like this?"

"That is because we cannot part from our homes where we have repeated birth-and-death for innumerable kalpas,[1] and do not long for the Pure Land we have not yet seen. Indeed, we are obsessed by delusions. Our minds are so thoroughly soaked with the scent of this world that they have become spiritually dull. So the only thing we can do is to take reluctant leave of this world and go to the Pure Land when our ties with this world have come to an end. When we are a little ill, we fear we may die. This is also due to our weaknesses and ignorance. That reminds me—Amida's great Vow is encouraging. Supposing we lacked this reluctance to enter the Pure Land; we might think we didn't have evil passions, and therefore, would not care about the great Vow of Amida."

Yuien-bo felt his doubt melting away like the spring thaw, as he listened to the Shonin's answer, which was spoken freely, without any artifice.

"Shonin, do you feel the same even at your age?"

"I feel just the same. No matter how old we may become, we are just as dull spiritually. A sparrow is a sparrow even if it lives a hundred years. We are the same unless we change our abode from here to the other land."

"Aren't you anxious to make a rebirth of the highest

[1] An infinite number of years.

degree?"

"I leave that matter to my Karma. I would like to die like an old sparrow, that's all."

Many years rolled by after this incident.

From about August in the second year of Kocho (1262), Shinran's health declined. Iyanyo and his disciples and followers grew worried. In November, his illness grew worse, and in the latter part of the month he was in critical condition.

Shinran's thread of life at the advanced age of ninety had been wearing out gradually, like that of an old tree.

When his illness grew serious, the Shonin only recited the Nembutsu. It was his expression of faith, recited naturally and continually.

Sometime before the "hour of the horse" (noon) his recitation stopped.

"When I die, put my body into the river Kamo and give it to the fish," he said.

Then he resumed his recitation. His words became indistinct, so the people at his bedside recited with him. At last his voice suddenly ceased. When they came close and looked at his face, they found that he had passed away into Nirvana.

It was at the hour of the horse on the 28th.[1] He lay on his right side with his head northward, and his face westward.

There were two messages left behind.

One was addressed to his disciples in Kanto:

[1] January 16, according to the present calendar.

" November, 2nd year of Kocho

I have grown old and am now ill. Soon I shall be reborn into the Pure Land, accomplishing my desire. Now I only wish to meet you all on the lotus seat of the Land of Bliss.

Respectfully yours,
Shinran "

The other was addressed to Shoshin-bo :

"November, 2nd year of Kocho

Even when my life comes to an end and I am reborn into the Pure Land, I will come back again and again, like the waves dashing on the beach of Waka-no-ura.[1] When one person rejoices, know that there are two who rejoice ; when two persons rejoice, there are three—for one of them is always Shinran.

Gutoku Shinran "

On the evening of the 29th, those who had waited on Shinran, such as Kenchi, Senshin, Renni, Iyanyo, and some layman followers, carried Shinran's body in a palanquin and left the gate of Zenbo-in. They went along the east bank of the Kamo River toward the western foot of the Higashiyama mountains, until they came to the graveyard of Enninji, at the southern end of Toribeno. There they laid the palanquin down.

These people, who had been present at Shinran's last moments and had strong spiritual ties with him, were filled with veneration and solemnity. They fell

[1] In Wakayama Prefecture.

on their knees and clasped their hands reverently. Then they cremated the remains and buried the ashes at Otani, not far away.

Ninety-year-old Shinran, fading and wishing to disapper like foam drifting on the waves of birth-and-death, thus finally entered Nirvana, the land of his desire.

After leading a long life in accordance with his Karma, he departed to start a new life in the Pure Land, where his savior Amida was preaching.

In his new life, he no longer had to repeat birth-and-death. It was an unchangeable, everlasting life, the " Boundless Life " and " Boundless Light " of Amida.

ON READING HYAKUZO KURATA'S
"SHINRAN"

By Saneatsu Mushakoji

I have just finished reading Hyakuzo Kurata's *Shinran*.

Reading it, I recalled my old friend Kurata. I could feel him everywhere in his writing. I began reading the book yesterday, and was so fascinated that I read the whole book. So last night I had a dream in which Kurata and I had a friendly talk. He had been one of my best friends.

Kurata, fascinated by Shinran ever since he had written *The Priest and His Disciples*, handled the material very well. The writing is straightforward and easy to understand, as may be expected of Kurata, who has many readers. We can easily understand Shinran's life and the era in which he lived. The author has not transformed Shinran through imagination, or over-praised him so as to make him look superhuman; he has created a warm-hearted Shinran who understands the sorrows and loneliness of life.

There are sections, however, which I wish he had developed more fully. But on the other hand, the book has become a sound one, which anyone can read without misunderstanding.

I wish that Shinran's life in Kyoto (in the last part of the book) had been written with more stress laid on Shinran. But I think the author correctly understood Shinran's reasons for coming back to Kyoto, and his feelings after returning there.

The scene where Shinran parts from his second wife and children is described sympathetically. However, I do not think Shinran's motives for abandoning his wife and children are adequately described.

I can understand Kurata's sympathetic view of Shinran's relationship with his son, but this view is commonplace. I think the author should have taken a more subjective view.

The author says in his preface that the stories of Iyanyo, Sho-amidabutsu, and Lady Hingashi that appear near the end are pure fiction, and I rather think that he must have enjoyed writing them. But to me, reading the book in order to know more about Shinran, this section is absurd. If Kurata were alive, I'm sure he would contradict me, but this section is different in tone from the rest; and those who read the book for religious education would be a little disappointed, I think.

But if this section were cut out, the book might make interesting reading.

The author says with confidence: " The work and interest of the author were focused on compiling a story by using all the available literature and free imagination. And I believe the story has grasped the essence of Shinran Shonin's character and faith."

What I admire is that Shinran Shonin's character and faith have been described clearly. I do not know whether the true Shinran was like the one described here, but I think it is interesting that Shinran and Kurata are both living in the book.

Moreover, the geographical locations are clear, and we can form a brief idea of Shinran's life. I am glad to be able to learn the legends about Shinran, at least. No other person can grasp and express Shinran's spirit so well, I think.

It was a very good thing that Kurata had written this book, which is irreplaceable.

The place where Shinran compares himself with Honen is interesting, for it makes me feel that here Kurata is thinking about himself. To avoid any misunderstanding, Kurata has written of Shinran's virtues as accurately as possible, which I believe is necessary in a book of this kind. I enjoyed the book and felt that my heart was cleansed by reading it.

I think this is a good book for anyone who wishes to know about Shinran.

HYAKUZO KURATA

Hyakuzo Kurata was born in 1891 in Hiroshima Prefecture, and died in 1943. Illness forced him to leave Daiichi Koto Gakko (First Higher school).

Ai to ninshiki to no shuppatsu (The Starting Point of Love and Cognition) was published at this time in the First Higher School alumni magazine.

In 1914 he joined Tenko Nishida's Ittoen, a humanitarian group, and subsequently, though bedridden by illness, published many unique dramas dealing with religion, ethics, and social themes.

His essays were written for the young men of coming generations.

Among his works besides the above are: *Seishun no iki no ato* (Traces of Youthful Breaths), *Shukke to sono deshi** (The Priest and His Disciples), *Shunkan, Fuse taishi no nyusen* (Prince Fuse's Entering Priesthood), *Seishi* (Contemplation), *Chokoku* (Overcoming Difficulties), *Zettaiteki seikatsu* (An Absolute Life), and *Shinran*.

---

* Translated into English by Glenn W. Shaw, June 1912—Hokuseido Press.